*My Neckline
and the Collapse of Western Civilization*

My Neckline and the Collapse of Western Civilization

Stories and Poems by Nine Bay Area Women

Smartweed Press

Typeset by Cragmont Publications, Oakland, California
Printed by Edwards Brothers, Inc.
Manufactured in the United States of America

Some of the poems and stories collected in *My Neckline and the Collapse of Western Civilization* appeared previously in publications as noted below.

"The Moon Snail," *Tunnel Road*, John F. Kennedy University Press, Orinda, CA. Copyright © 1979 by Sue Heath Brown.

"On Being Told Aunt Agnes Saved Uncle Roland's Life with Mouth-to-Mouth Resucitation," *Womanblood*, Continuing Saga Press, San Francisco, CA. Copyright © 1981 by Alice Wirth Gray.

"Snow White and the Man Sent to Fetch Her Heart." Poetry Society of America *Bulletin*, New York, N.Y., The Gordon Barber Memorial Award. Copyright © 1981 by Alice Wirth Gray.

"Mr. Ferris Reports on Technological Progress: From the Nile, 1886," *Cedar Rock*, New Braunfels, Tx. Copyright © 1979 by Alice Wirth Gray.

"Fallen Giant," Arvon International Poetry Competition *Anthology*, Devon, England. A Duncan Lawrie Prize. Copyright © 1987 by Alice Wirth Gray.

"City Poem at Night," *Impact*, The Commentators' Press, Sunnyvale, CA. Copyright © 1979 by Mary L. Hanner.

"Delivery" and "Debut," *Cedar Rock*, New Braunfels, Tx. Copyright © 1978 by Mary L. Hanner.

"The Berry Patch," *Impact*, The Comentators' Press, Sunnyvale, CA. Copyright © 1979 by Mary Tolman Kent.

"Jack Murphy," "Irma," "At Newport School," "Ramona," "Jewel," "Mrs. Green," "Big Brother," "Elaine," "Daddy," "Little Brother," *Cedar Rock*, New Braunfels, Tx. Copyright © 1979 by Mollie Poupeney.

"The Voyage," *Blue Unicorn*, Kensington, CA. Copyright © 1987 by Jane Strong.

Library of Congress Cataloging–in–Publication Data

My neckline and the collapse of western civilization.

    1. American literature—California—San Francisco Bay Area.
2. American literature—Women authors. 3. American literature—20th century.
4. Women and literature—California—San Francisco Bay Area.
5. San Francisco Bay Area (Calif.)—Literary collections. I. Brown, Sue Heath,
1921–   . II. Kent, Mary, 1921–   . III. Zalkin, Maxine, 1930–
PS572.S33M9   1987   810 '.8'09287   87–12915
ISBN 0–9617736–0–X

Stories and Poems

Thank you

Jack

Annie

Claire Josefine

Sarah

Preface

by Michael Rubin

Imagine asking a man to introduce a collection of poetry and prose written by women. True, four of the writers in here were hostage to my fiction workshops at the University of California Extension in Berkeley during the mid–70's. All the more reason to feel pleased that our work together reached out to the other writers you'll soon meet in here.

Memory, however, like fiction, plays tricks, so those women might also hold this recall against me: Mollie Poupeney, with her you–can't–tell–me–nothin' grin, taking in our critiques of her loggers and Oregon drunks. Alice Gray, her round face all pouts, her sweet voice all doubts, and all designed to disarm us before slicing forth with her shrewd insights, sly wit. Sue Brown, at first glance seeming as cozy as her All American name—until her pain–filled distractions compel a much closer look at her writing. And Dorothy Stroup, heir to Margaret Sullavan's pageboy and Virginia Woolf's tragic–edged eyes, already so deeply engaged in her long struggle to capture the intricate legacy of Hiroshima after its devastation.

How did these four find the five other Bay Area women whose work fill these pages? And how did their remarkably durable Tuesday Writers' Group get started at all? Well, as far as I can figure, during my several workshops, Dorothy met Sue, Mollie met Alice, Sue met Mollie who also met Dorothy who, through a later workshop given by Jeffrey Klein, also met Mary Kent. Now, Mary Kent and Mollie were already part of a burgeoning writing group that had grown out of Susan Griffin's 1974 U.C. offering, "Women's Voices, a Writing Workshop," whose members also included Mary McLaughlin and Mary Hanner, all three Marys eventually hailed into this book. Mary Kent met Jane Strong in Susan Griffin's second class and Maxine Zalkin from still one more U.C. workshop.

All of this, note well, began coming together over thirteen years ago now. And the sheer length of time that the core group has prevailed is cause enough for wonder. Thirteen years of weekly meetings. Thirteen years of commitment to one another as well as to their own work—not to mention their families and lovers and friends. "If this is Tuesday, it must be the Group," quips Jane Strong. All those Tuesday afternoons, year in and out, devoted to listening to each other read from their latest efforts, to discussing what each has shared, to cheering and clapping, and knocking and scrapping, to exchanging much more than the poetry and prose they produced.

What could possess them?

Indeed, some do sound possessed:

Sue Brown: "Joining the Group... was like falling in love. My whole awareness expanded, I became more alive, more sensitive, more energized... "

Mary Hanner: "Sometimes I say all the names... Alice... Jane... Mollie... Mary... like a religious naming saints or breathing prayers on wondrous opalescent beads... I think perhaps we are a family of sisters... "

Mollie Poupeney: "I have said to the Group This is my church. This is my magic circle. This group is sacred."

But writers are usually paradoxical souls so doubt can easily vie with devotions:

"Maybe it's a basic weakness rather than strength that holds us together," Sue Brown also muses.

"How could it hurt you, something so pleasant, so loving, so amusing, so maddening, such fun?" Jane Strong wonders, "— unless it made us feel that we had given up communication with a wider audience to settle for a substitute, a surrogate, a sweetener of failure... ?"

Maxine Zalkin: "I am strongly suspicious of groups' being able to soothe or cajole individual integrity out of people. I have a fear of what I call the 'Improvement Club Syndrome'... in which only those who agree will stay around until everyone agrees that the world is square."

Nonetheless, for better or worse, week after week, year after year, these women and their co–members return. Though they may praise it or blame it, they are sure of their gain:

Mary Kent: "In the beginning we simply shared the desire to overcome our reticence, to build each other's self–confidence, but in time we became clear about what it was we were wanting to say, we became better listeners, critics, writers."

Maxine Zalkin: "I have come to value constructive criticism even more than pats on the back, and have grown from an extremely shy, introverted person to a more confident person because of it."

Alice Gray: "I'd never have learned how to send things out if there hadn't been people in the group who were way ahead of me who told us how it was done. We also talk about our lives, because we like stories and because sometimes we need to get rid of the emotional garbage that accumulates in order to be free to write. There's no place I feel freer to talk about anything and everything (sex and death) than at the group. 'Gossip' is what people call it when women talk to each other in an attempt to understand how the world is put together and works. I think it's essential and if it were Norman Mailer talking the same way to a male author, it would be an 'important conversation.'"

Mollie Poupeney: "Over the years I've learned to trust my work to be exposed to the perceptions and judgments of the people in the Group, and also to trust myself not to be impelled to act on any criticism that doesn't feel right to me. I trust the honesty, the intelligence, and also (and this is very important) the appreciation that is given me as a contributing member. I believe we show one another that appreciation by our loyalty to one another, our mutual respect, and our freedom to disagree in good conscience."

Mary Hanner: "When I go to the group I always come home with a shiny pebble in my pocket. Sometimes I towed a boulder. Other times it was more like a coating of dust. Few of us go away empty–handed. I learned that writing is important. It can move the world, bring back the dead, remake history, and foretell the future."

Is this anthology then, simply the press of communal vanity? More a testament to supportive friends than to their art? Not from what I've read. Although love and respect have helped sustain this group through the years, each individual's talent is clearly in evidence here. Nor is much of the work of this group known only among themselves. Its members have had many occasions to celebrate the publication of each other's novels and poems and short stories. From this generous collection you will learn why.

What's in it?

Well, as Dorothy Stroup sat listening to the group's work over the years, she remembers gazing at Mary Kent's and Alice Gray's livingroom rugs, and the "patterns which adapt themselves to the story or poem being read, opening up depths that lead to oceans, skies, and other expansions... In them are all the myriad lives: a drunken Irish lumberjack on the coast of Oregon; a pair of parents following their hippie child on a pilgrimage deep into the interior of the Mendocino woods; a young girl in Ireland listening to her father recite the lines of an Irish play... "

You'll find those situations in here weaving themselves into stories and poems, as well as so many others: an old man both perplexed and rather pleased by a romance; a woman, afraid of a rat, being courted by another and stranger one over the phone; a grandmother finding herself adventuring just a little bit further than her old berry patch; a group of Japanese and American poetry buffs searching for an exactitude of the spirit that seems to elude the best of translations; a virtual northwestern Spoon River anthology, moon snails, spring wells, a Jewish brother, blue eyes, bath water, mouth–to–mouth resuscitation, continuing education, cabbage babies, dragonflies, autumn grass.... "All of these are woven into the squares of Mary's rug," Dorothy Stroup fancies. "And into Alice's too...where a branch of blossoms reaches out and ensnares us into its mysteries... "

Beyond all the good mysterious stuff in store here, the discerning reader may also see the publication of this anthology as an admirable act of empowerment. In an age when too many fine writers are left standing among the musical chairs that editors play at publishing houses; or find their manuscripts under consideration suddenly returned by book companies dissolving in mergers; or watch with dismay when what they have even finally published goes unadvertised, undistributed, shredded before it's had any shelf life at all, the enterprise that this book represents can stand as an inspiration to other writing groups and individual authors. Smaller local presses, regional co–ops, self–publishers, and communal ventures like this all may encourage writers to pursue less traditional ways of reaching the public they merit.

Of course, with all in the world that works against it, the Tuesday group, like all writers, also occasionally wonder just why they still do it. Two of their answers stay with me, and deserve the last word:

Mary Hanner again brings in the group: "I love all those ceramic animals at Mollie's house, Mary's Irish soda bread, those crisp apples Sue cuts up on a blue and white plate, the wonderful rug at Alice's house, steamed milk in a white pitcher at Mary Kent's—we love the details because we are compelled to make sense of the world and write it down before we die. Or forget it. No one gives a hang if an adverb were better left out."

But group or no group, "it still comes down to why do you write," Jane Strong insists. And "since we can't answer 'for the money' there must be another reason which can operate on a rainy day as well as a sunny one. It has something to do with change, with risk, with pleasure as well as pain. It's a field with new challenges, with surprise, discoveries, and sometimes even with a great surge of joy."

Alice Wirth Gray

My Neckline and the Collapse of Western Civilization

"One must always have a little white at the throat."
"Why, Grandma?" I had trouble imagining what "white–
at–the–throat" meant, having as yet no pearls. I thought
of the white stripes painted around tree trunks to keep bugs off.
My dresses did all have a little white collar in ugly contrast to the
rest of the fabric. I assumed this had something to do with "dirt,"
a big subject with Grandma. Life was full of subtleties: apparently
one must have *some* white but one might never have an all–white
dress because it would "show every spot."

Grandma answered, "Because."

My fifth grade teacher said, "I never tell you to do something just 'because'. I always give a reason." It was clear Miss
Billingsly had been to a summer session at the University's School
of Education and had learned "children need to feel the teacher
respects them." I sensed there was more to it: she wanted adora-
tion and offered an alliance that would set me in conflict with my
mother and grandmother whom I would recognize to be lacking
by the light of her example. A dangerous lure! Still, the premise
was interesting and worth testing. I tried Grandma again.

"*Why* must one wear white at the throat?"

"Don't you sass me, Miss. I told you, just because."

So I knew "White–at–the–throat" was one of those beliefs on
which Grandmother's deepest feelings of superiority rested, by
which she could be picked out as better than others as dogs or
cats sniff each other's bottoms to determine their relative social
position. White–at–the–throat mattered in inverse proportion to
Grandmother's ability to explain why. It told good girls from bad
as did the heinous piercing of ears which Grandmother said only
Negroes or Catholics did. I was glad my ears were not pierced,
not because I had a Puritan objection to ornament nor moral con-

victions about mutilation of the body, but because I was a sniveling coward so fearful of needles that I crawled under my parents' bed and screamed and held onto the box springs from the underside and had to be pushed out with a broom by Mother whenever Dr. Karpstein stopped by the house to give me a vitamin shot. If there were a heaven, and my family, being atheists, knew there was not, pierced ears would exclude one from it. Fine by me!

Mother's social litmus tests were not the same as Grandma's, but she had them. She completely dismissed a beautiful woman with "Well, but she's thirty–five and wears her hair down to her shoulders!" Recent developments in my life convinced me Mother should tread softly here. There was the possibility people who knew this rule, No Long Unbound Hair after Thirty–five Even If It's Not Gray, would betray you, would not join in shunning the unworthy creature, but continue to regard her as an acceptable person and turn on you to ask "What does it matter? Why do *you* care?" and you would be stuck. I knew the woman in question was Mademoiselle Tremaine, the new French teacher at my school, and the prettiest person I'd ever seen. My new perceptions told me any woman in her right mind should study Mademoiselle carefully, from her free–swinging black hair to her high sling heels. In another household, Mother's snub might have begun "No lady ever..." but Mother prided herself on having overcome the prejudices of her Southern background. She'd taken up Socialism and couldn't be caught making invidious judgments based on social class.

I grew alert to these taboos, as when Mother and I walked in the neighborhood, admiring the old houses, and we passed a favorite and mother began to wail "Oh, they've ruined it! Ruined it! How could they?" I stared, expecting the fine stone had been covered with aluminum siding or a dump of crushed cans and rotting garbage was rising in the yard, but all looked stately as ever. The offense was they'd hung red curtains in the windows. Very cheerful, I thought, but it was somehow Wrong.

What gave me independent ideas on these things was the growth of my breasts. This began when I was not yet ten, accompanied by such pain that I was forced to mention it to Mother. She did not take me to Dr. Karpstien, but to the school doctor who was a woman. Dr. Ford began to tell me I was Developing and would soon Become a Woman and so on and on while I said to myself "So *that's* all it is! What a relief!" It was just I'd had no idea it could hurt so, but knowing the cause, I no longer cared how painful it was; I was wild to be grown up. What it would get me, I wasn't sure, but I was ready to find out. Mother seemed torn between satisfaction at my precosity and horror that it was Not Polite and people would say it's what she got for marrying a Jew: a daughter who would mature too soon, pierce her ears and run away with Gypsies. By the time sweet flatchested unmarried Dr. Ford finished her speech, I'd discovered my breasts had an effect on the world that I could use. In science class, when I leaned across the workbench to pass a microscope slide to Eric, Miss Pugloff sent me out of the room. I knew why and laughed. There was nothing frightening about my friends Laura or Nadine, but I had the power to scare the wits out of Miss Pugloff. And she was obliged to come invite me back to the classroom: she couldn't lock out one of her best students, not at this expensive private school. All she could do was comfort herself nice girls didn't grow such big breasts so soon. My breasts, I observed, were immense, outrageous, a joke; but a joke that did not make the boys laugh. On the contrary, Eric and the others all competed to have me for their lab partner, were willing to spend hours with me learning the orbits of the planets or the Linneaean classifications, and ready to stay any length of time after school on special projects and do most of the work, too. A blissful arrangement, and just in time to keep me from dying of boredom! When my sixth grade math report card came, I understood no one was immune:

> "She seems to have lost interest in her work. She would rather talk to the boys and I'm sure she distracts them. She can spend an hour 'caressing' her pencil and gazing out the window in that maddening way of hers, when she could have completed the compound interest and square root sections of her workbook in a third of the time by actually working as I told her. Today she was very impertinent and refused to work alone on the opposite side of the room from the boys. Unless she is willing to work and quit her gossip, I do not want her in my class."   Oscar H. Dove

Mother extended this sheet of paper to me without comment when I got home. "Gracious," I said, "He is all wrought up, isn't he?" Mr. Dove was our only male teacher. I knew there was nothing he could do about me either, and I felt sorry for him but his report taught me my first modicum of caution: I had a serious weapon and should not be stupid about using it. Mother regarded me thoughtfully and I was never again completely helpless in one of our frequent arguments.

I knew now where I stood: the path of white–at–the–throat was not mine. Ancient Miss Sims who wore a hat in class retired. Hired to replace her was Mademoiselle Tremaine, she of the shiny hair to the shoulders though she was thirty–five. Nadine's mother said the hair was a skillful dye job, but that didn't alter Mademoiselle's beauty, and she wore not a speck of white but, rather, a tight black dress with a deep–cut square neck with a half–inch of fuchsia ruching. Where this nestled into the cleft between her breasts, she sported a We Want Wilkie button and, just above it, on a thin gold chain, a tiny gold cross. A Cross! Never had I seen a teacher or fellow student wear a religious symbol but perhaps only a Catholic could teach French? My classmates were Protestants with a sprinkling of Jews; there was not a Catholic or a cross to be seen. It was, like red curtains or pierced ears or big breasts, not done. The Wilkie button soon vanished Mademoiselle quickly apprehended that although most of us were rich, we were all from the families of Democrats with the exception of Barry whose father was a liberal Republican advertising executive. But the cross remained.

Our mothers could snicker at Mademoiselle Tremaine, but I saw her in the hall after school try to pass Mr. Dove who grabbed her and backed her up against the wall and kissed her. She laughed and pushed at him gently, but there were tears running down his cheeks. Our secret advantage wasn't funny.

Tsk, tsk. Mr. Dove's wife has been acting odd. She also teaches at my school. Every morning in her home economics class we watch her dandruff flake off into the white sauce or the *pâte à choux*. Attendance reports are taken in every class every hour, not for discipline or for reporting to the state numbers of heads taught, but because many of us would bring a big ransom, and

Mrs. Dove has taken to calling the richest parents and saying their child has not arrived at school and must have been kidnapped. Mrs. Dove, we have been informed, is going to a nice place where she can get the help she needs to get well, but I know she's a hopeless case or why would her husband *cry* while kissing Mademoiselle Tremaine? My breasts give me this understanding. Grownups kissing in the hall! How thrilling! Years and years of pleasure stretch before me, far beyond fumbling with Albert or Eric or Seth in the cloakroom; and the bigger the breasts, the bigger the opportunities. My neckline would give me insight into the workings of the whole world.

Mother said to me, "What do you make of this? Last night's PTA meeting was an overflow crowd. We had to move into the auditorium. I've never seen so many men turn out for New Teachers' Night. I'm glad your dad could come: I'd have been embarrassed alone. That Tremaine woman would be attractive if she'd cut her hair and not show so much of her front. I hear she's not really a particularly good French teacher, but somehow everyone came to meet her. Can you beat that?"

Mademoiselle was, in fact, an exceptionally lousy French teacher, but you wouldn't hear it from me. We were sisters from the neck down.

Alice Wirth Gray

Fallen Giant

An incense cedar bit the dust
in that great storm, had a tantrum,
threw itself on the ground. No one
was under it, but could have been,
and my hand shook, dialing the City.
A crew came with chain saws,
cleared the street and stacked huge logs
beside the house. My husband
mourned by the ruins and this woman
slides by, confronts him:
Did you do that? Did you cut down
that tree? She is really out to get him,
damn him, he hates trees,
she can tell, and she knows he hates
all living things: it's men like him,
tall, with hair on their bodies,
who kill whales barehanded.
I see all her simplistic politics,
know what she does in bed and her whole
stimulus–and–response life. She's never
lost a loving tree. Never come to question
the stability of all trees because one
has fallen, known the awesome many
there are when one comes to doubting.
She's brave, give her that, attacking
a big man who holds an ax. My husband
tells her patiently of armillaria,
the oakroot fungus, offers to show her
fruiting bodies and wood decay
until she's relieved to get away,
sorry she tried to take him on,

not knowing his relentless kindness
to women, his unalterable love
of conifers. And meanwhile, how
shall we silence the remaining tree?
It has set up such a great sighing,
a lamentation for its mate.

Alice Wirth Gray

On Being Told Aunt Agnes
Saved Uncle Roland's Life with
Mouth-to-Mouth Resuscitation

We didn't even know you liked him, Auntie.
What we've known of you has been
so strictly clean and brittle;
we remember when you had the windows
sealed and airconditioning put in
to keep the dust off the flocks
of Dresden milkmaids that tiptoed
across your parlor tables. We knew
you dusted their frozen lace petticoats
with a sable brush. Whatever Uncle Roland
was or is, he's no china shepherdess.
Deputy sheriff, forest ranger, hunter,
red–faced beer–drinking slob, onceuponatime
lover of a woman whose husband, we hear,
still wallops her because of it
after forty years. That woman's broken,
short of breath. But you, Aunt Agnes,
who knew you had any breath at all,
much less to spare? Our eyes stop
no longer at your glazed hair:
we see inside you a strong, free–moving
column of air and you astride Uncle
on the Wilton carpet, pumping, riding him
for all you're worth, giving him something
after all.

Alice Wirth Gray

I Become a Sinister Character

They tore down the old Post Office
and moved into new quarters nearby.
The same three guys who've weighed my poems
and sold me stamps for years
are now behind bulletproof glass
and there's a little hole too high
for me to speak into without shouting,
and a trough for me to stick my money in
not big enough for hand or gun;
and to mail a book to my sister in LA
I have to open this panel,
put the package in there,
and close the panel and wait until
one of them opens a second panel
on the other side and takes my gift out
so they're never exposed to danger.
Although I don't know how they'd tell
if there were a bomb in my parcel
instead of Susanna Moore's *My Old Sweetheart*,
unless there's an x-ray device
in the compartment that would indicate
if there were. The three men,
who've always been sourpusses,
although this is a pleasant neighborhood
and their jobs look comfortable and easy,
if a little dull, are now raised
on a platform behind unbreakable glass,
and they yell down at me through the hole.
Funny, I've never wanted to shoot a postman
before.

Alice Wirth Gray

Mr. Ferris Reports on Technological Progress: from the Nile, 1886

Tall singing black women muscled like killing vines
advance down the Nile.
A traffic signal turns against them;
they keep their feet in motion,
trucking, strutting, sashaying, pumping
shimmying bopping swaying, hardly moving.
I smile: these primitive creatures think
if they stop moving, they'll sink,
and there are crocodiles. Their big feet
in Carmen Miranda cork–soled sandals with bright straps,
Rita Hayworth rope–soled platform wedgies,
don't dent the river's surface.
The sun, their vitality hold them up.
They wait as if before an invisible gate.
The light's red: a freight–laden side–wheeler
churns cross–river in a Turner-foam,¯
spray green yellow white blue gray,
colors cold as fog, fact hot as a steam laundry.
The red and black stack passes above,
the wake washes against the women,
almost swamps them,
stoic, they struggle to steady themselves, stay upright,
only the tick of their shoes skittering on the water
speeds up, the scratchy sound of small snakes
met in dry deserts.
They keep their balance.
I catch the eye of the tallest.
Turner had no feeling for flesh,
only for mist rising.

The light turns green. They proceed,
drawn down the Nile
as water evaporates toward the sun,
baskets of sticky moogli fruit on their heads.
I touch my hand to the Sultan's jewelled sleeve:
Why do they walk on the water?
He says it's because they move their feet so quickly.
It is so difficult with no interpreter.
No, I shake my head, I am an engineer,
and I understand all that.
But it is very backward:
they should not walk on the water.
The women wear mud plaster matted into their hair,
the custom in their country.
The Sultan shrugs: Walking on the river
is a prerogative of their caste,
that and the secrets of cultivating the moogli fruit.
This last is an interesting process:
the seeds are the size of elephants,
the bushes quite small.
When the fruit is the size of a cashew
it becomes salty enough for my people to eat.
They dislike sweet. The plant is dug, root and all...
The Sultan is conscientiously informative,
but his sole wish is to rest in the shade,
watching the laborers, enduring the heat,
until construction is complete,
awaiting the day when the music will play
and my great wheel will begin turning, turning,
gasoline burning, hung with bells and lanterns,

knotted with the sweet flowers of river rushes,
and the Sultan and his rotund little wives
will fasten themselves with ruby velvet ropes
into the dangling baskets
and go spinning round and round the night sky
in my exploded star of steel,
round and round like the paddlewheel
while a separate engine spews confetti
of gold and silver leaf.
When the wheel turns, I've leave to go.

Down river the women insist in walking
on the deepest part of the channel,
their feet spinning like flywheels.
Why did the tallest one look back?
Ah, the Nile is a beautiful sight!
My travels give me much to ponder,
but this sticks in my craw:
why are these women allowed to interfere?
Why does the tallest one look back?

Alice Wirth Gray

Work Preferences

Poets and Writers, Inc.,
wants to know my work preferences.
Senior citizens, women,
blacks, prisoners, Native Americans,
gays or lesbians, highschool kids?
Sure, I nod, I've done some of that,
and will no doubt do more;
but in my heart I know
they've omitted my first choice.

I want to do workshops
for the very rich,
the kind where everyone comes
with a perfect-bound notebook
with no writing in it yet
and jacquärded flowers
on the cover and afterwards
they give you champagne
and little caviar sandwiches
and fuss over you and everyone
has Terribly Good Manners
and no one has any intention
of complicating things
by writing any poetry.

Alice Wirth Gray

The Egg Man, 1948

The old refugee who sold eggs door to door
came once at six AM, and Mother threw a fit:
God damn it, don't you know not to ring the bell
so early? His English couldn't handle much
but words like Fresh and Duck, so he took it,
standing there in the foyer under the fanlight
and chandelier, his eyes filling with tears.

Mother wasn't one who could say I'm sorry,
but after coffee she said off-handed to the cook,
she'd figured it was fall: we'd gone off
Daylight Savings, and he didn't know enough
to set his clock back.

Each year I set the clocks back.
I haven't missed yet, but you mustn't either:
because I can't bear you be criticized
for lack of any knowledge I could impart.
So I always ask each of you separately,
that Sunday, casually, as if it means nothing,
Oh, have you remembered to change your watch?

And each of you always looks up
with that exasperated roll of the eyes,
that What–does–it–matter–Mother?–look;
or else with a wicked smile of surprise,
and shrugs and says, No, I forgot.

Alice Wirth Gray

Snow White and the Man Sent to Fetch Her Heart

> "...she began to weep, and said:
> 'Ah, dear huntsman, leave me my life!
> I will run away into the wild forest,
> and never come home again.' "
>
> The Brothers Grimm

Think carefully. That's what
you said that did the trick?
It would be cruelty
to give us the wrong charm
when we get no second chance.
We know, of course, that you
were gorgeous. Was that all
it was, and you need not
have opened your mouth?

Perhaps he was a revolutionary,
set to do anything contrary
to the old Queen's interests.
Or else the death at his hands
each year of myriad stags, wolves
and quail quelled his bloodlust,
left him empty of hostility,
a peaceable kingdom all of himself.
His relationships with people
were impeccable. He worried
that abortion was really murder.

Perhaps he found you irresistible,
Snow White, and you promised him
something? And the whole
seamy story got suppressed
when your party came to power?
A nasty piece of business,
if you had the man done in
when he came for his pay–off;
or if you gave him what he wanted
and left us, poor suckers, thinking
it was all done with no *quid pro quo*,
turning the affair into something
like a press release for Evita Perón,
one of those tales that goes down
in countries where once a year
they haul the Virgin's statue
on a wagon and the hysterical poor
cover her with paper money the way
flies do sweet exudations.

Maybe you bargained with him:
The old Queen's on the way out.
Stick with me and you'll get
a stone cottage and be top hunter.
Just the truth, please,
the kind of information
that gives confidence
on the Subway: that we know
the right response to violence.
Was he, perhaps, unique;
and anyone else in the court

would, words or no, have had
your heart out, zip, and sizzling
on a stick, quick as a spark?
What's the Snow White approach
to paranoids, sociopaths
and sadists, the sure cure
for peer pressure? Or were you
just lucky?

Was there some threat:
The man I marry will be King
and if you lay a hand on me,
he'll have your skin? Or,
did your little hand whistle
through the air in a karate chop
that recalled to him
how tender is the groin?
Snow White, we don't want
to make the wrong move
when there's a sure-fire way
to handle the situation. What
do you say to keep the world
from having your heart out?

Mollie Poupeney

Big Benny Olson and the Kid Marine

I was tending bar the night Big Benny Olson first met up with Wilbur, the kid Marine. The way the kid Marine was slurring and leering his face down the bar I could see Big Benny thinking the kid was making lewd and lascivious remarks to his girl, Charmain, even though you couldn't hear a word what with the noise from the jukebox and the crowd hanging around the pool table. Me, I wouldn't swear to this day that Wilbur was actually saying anything out of line, but the looks he was sending Charmain's way were definitely *not* what you'd call sweet. Around here everybody knows that Benny's big as a grizzly but gentle as a lamb. That don't mean he'd let *nobody*, friend nor enemy, insult his girl, lady or no lady, and this kid, Wilbur, was definitely no friend to these parts.

"I hear one more word out of you and I pull off both your legs and stuff em up your ass," Benny says, his voice low and quiet, almost gentle as he taps the kid on the shoulder. Wilbur's sort of sunk into the top of the bar, one arm barely holding up his head.

"Yeah?" That kid's face crinkles up into his widest grin and he starts laughing so hard at Benny you couldn't hear a sound out of him. He's shaking all over the stool until he falls right on the floor at Benny's feet. Then he just lays there laughing and pounding on his leg with his knuckles like he's knocking on the door.

"Yeah," Benny says.

"Oh, Yeah?" Wilbur squeals, "knock, knock!" Then he collapses again on Benny's shoes. Benny just stands there looking down.

"Knock, knock," he squeaks some more, his fist cracking his knuckles on his leg again like he's hitting pure bone.

Benny looks across the bar at me. "What the hell's the matter with him, Chuck?" he asks me. "Is he crazy, or what?"

"All I know's he's an ex–Marine," I say, figuring that's enough explanation for anybody who wasn't born yesterday. I take the empty Bud bottle out of his hand and give him a fresh one, but Benny, his face all screwed up with trying to understand, don't seem to notice.

"God, he don't look like no Marine I ever seen," he says. "He's too goddam scrawny."

"I know for a fact he was. He was in here the other night waving some citation around says he got shot up pretty good at Khe Sahn."

"Khe Sahn?" Benny says and pulls himself up tall and shifts his belt a little lower, loosening his balls. "Where's that?"

"You know—over there in Vietnam."

"Oh, yeah, that's where all them Marines got shot up, ain't it?" Then he strains every fiber of his Can't Bustems and squats down and peers into Wilbur's face. The kid's eyes are shut and he's having his own private glee club right there on the floor. "Shit, kid—Khe Sahn, huh? You're a hero, so how come you're acting like some goddam asshole? Get up and knock it off and I'll buy you a beer."

Wilbur was unbending and grabbing for the rungs of stools now and got himself up on his feet. Benny brushes the cigarette butts and crap off the kid's shoulder and asks, "What'll you have?"

"Knock, knock," the kid grins again, and before we know what the hell he's doing he unbuttons his jeans right there in front of God and everybody and reaches inside.

"Oh, for Chrissake, not here," Benny says when he sees the kid's hand doing something over by his hip beneath his jockey shorts. Then he sits down on the stool, grabs his foot, gives a funny jerk, and honest to God, we're all standing there watching this kid pull off his left leg.

"Holy shit," Benny mumbles, staring at that shiny leg with all the steel gadgets.

"You—you—wanna shove it up my ass?" Wilbur snorts through the snickering snot, "you wanna? Go ahead, big man! Be my guest!"

Then the kid collapses again on Benny's boots.

"Holy shit, it comes off," Benny says. "What's that kid doing with only one leg, Chuck?"

"I told you he was a Marine. I guess that's what the disability's all about. Like I said he's only been in here one other time, the other night—"

"Benny!" Charmain is pulling on his arm. "C'mon, let's go. You said we was gonna have a good time—leave him, he ain't nothing to bother with—" I can see she's not going to budge him from that spot no more than a piss ant could move a tree stump.

"For chrissake, Charmain, we can't leave him here like that. The damn kid's only got one leg!" Benny says, staring down at Wilbur cuddling his phony leg to his cheek now like he was singing it a lullaby. His eyes are closed and he isn't laughing anymore, and if the truth were told, I swear to God I think the kid was crying.

Benny keeps saying, "Holy shit, this ain't right. Look at that little bastard—" Which is what we were all doing now, looking and listening to Wilbur cry. The jukebox had quit a long time ago.

"Who wants to spend a Saturday night sitting around listening to some damn drunk crying in his beer?" Charmain said. "C'mon, let's get our butts outa here. We got better things to do with our time. Benny? C'mon, Benny—"

But Benny don't hear Charmain. He leans down and scoops Wilbur and his plastic leg up in his arms and heads for the door. Charmain asks him just where the hell does he think he's going, but Benny walks right past her like she was dirt, which I happen to know she is, and that was the last I ever seen of the kid Marine.

I don't find out about Benny being in jail until two o'clock the next afternoon, and when I go to see him it's a different Benny sitting on that cot in the cell, his face white as chalk and his eyes looking at me like two burnt holes in a blanket. But he don't look like no murderer, not to me, anyhow.

"What the hell happened, Benny?" I ask him. "I mean, for Chrissake, the sheriff says you killed somebody, or it looks that way—"

Benny's staring at me like he don't understand a word I'm saying, so I ask him again, quieter, the way you ask a little kid that's too scared to talk.

"C'mon, Benny, I'm your friend, you can tell me—just tell me what happened—was it that kid Marine, or what? What happened after you left the bar last night?"

Well, it took awhile, but little by little Benny starts telling me the story.

He carries the kid out to the parking lot, Benny says, and he props Wilbur up against Benny's new Mach I and somehow gets his leg hooked up so's everything's working again. But as soon as Benny gets Wilbur's pants zipped, Wilbur begins unzipping again.

"Hey, what the hell you doing?" Benny says. "I just got through putting you together."

"Gotta peepeepee eye ess," Wilbur says, and aims for the stars just a little to the left of Benny. He's making those "eheheheh" sounds like he's aiming that new automatic submachine gun all the Marines carried around like they was toothpicks over in Nam. Then he seems to take notice of Benny for the first time and cranes his neck up to check out who it is he's passing water with.

"Yessir, sarge," he says, "yessir, I got 'em all just like you said, every mother and child, just like you said—" And he gives Benny a sloppy salute and grins.

"What the hell you talking about? You don't make sense, son."

"Not your son, sarge—not nobody's son. No sons in the Marines. Nossir. Nope. Marines got no mamas, got no daddys. Only got sarges and lieutenants and their fucking M 2's," Wilbur says and starts snickering again. The kid's weaving and sliding on the slippery green metal flake finish of the new car and Benny reaches out his hand to balance the kid against the racing stripe.

"How long you been a Marine?" he asks.

"I was born a Marine, sir!" Wilbur barks in his gyrene voice, which knocks him off balance and he begins to slide. Benny puts him on the spot again and laughs.

"Christ, you're just a kid! What the hell they doing with kids?"

And this is where Wilbur's fist hits Benny in the groin. When he's doubled over his gut, Wilbur chops him in the kidney, and Benny drops to the asphalt, sucking air. Now it's Benny's turn to be on the ground looking up, and he sees Wilbur standing tall, looking down.

"Jesus," he groans, "what's going on?"

"You mess with me, big man, you'll wake up with a pungie stick up your ass, no sweat!"

Benny groans again. "Christ, he's just a kid!" he tells the asphalt under his nose, then doubles up again with a sharp kick to the same spot in the groin. "Oh, my God!" he moans, "What's with you? You crazy, or something?"

"I'm a Marine, sir!" Wilbur shouts.

Benny gets up slow, holding his groin, and leans against the car beside Wilbur, keeping his eye on the kid all the time.

"You're faster'n shit," he gasps, "Where the hell did you learn that?"

"I'm a M—"

"Never mind. I know where you learnt it—"

"—arine, sir!"

"You're like a goddam rattlesnake—which leg did you kick me with?"

Wilbur only smiles, like it was nobody's business, as long as it got the job done, which it had.

"Christ," Benny says, "I'd like to have my old man meet you sometime. He wouldn't believe you—" The kid gyrene has Benny going, being so little and packing a wallop that would make Benny's old man stand in line begging for lessons. And everybody around here knows old Eugene Olson was tough. I seen him more than once put Benny up against the wall with Benny's feet almost off the ground, and it wasn't that long ago. Not that Benny, big as a bear, couldn't've pounded both his old man and the kid Marine into snuff if he'd wanted to, but the trouble with

Benny was that he just didn't have a mean streak in him anywhere. That's why his old man kicked him around. Old Eugene
was ashamed to have a boy as big as Benny not taking advantage
of his God given gifts of size and strength. And Benny had the
scars to prove it. Eugene couldn't get Benny to fight back even
when he was roaring drunk on a Saturday night, even when he
shot out Benny's first set of Michelins on his new Mach I with the
thirty aught six, which he had done the same week Benny'd
bought the car. I know. I was there. And the thing about it was
that Benny's old man wasn't much bigger'n Wilbur.

"You gotta meet my old man," Benny says.

And that was when Wilbur pitches over on his face and
passes out cold and Benny collects him in his arms again and
places him in the backseat of his Mach I. He peels out of the parking lot past the sugar beet Coop and the train depot and heads
down the highway. When he turns into the driveway and parks
behind the house, he sees it's dark which means the old man's
probably passed out in the front bedroom, snoring and blowing
as usual. Benny carries Wilbur, still out cold, into the house and
turns on a light.

The living room's its usual mess with clothes and newspapers and hunting rifles laying around. The white paint on the
walls and woodwork look like they'd been varnished with ni-
cotine, and over the couch is the black hole in the wall where the
old man's twelve gauge shotgun went off one night, nobody's
saying how. Benny sneaks past old Eugene's door to his own bedroom and lays out the kid Marine, making sure both his legs are
stretched out straight, and covers Wilbur with the afghan Benny's
Ma crocheted the year before she died.

"Sleep good," he says, "In the morning I'm gonna introduce
you to my old man."

Then he makes it to the couch in the living room, sits down
and looks around, smiling to himself, until he sees the mess the
room is in. It wouldn't do, he decides, to have the place like a pig-
pen when it was time for him to introduce his new friend to his
old man, so he scoops up the newspapers, Eugene's socks and
boots and the jelly jars full of chewing tobacco spit, also the six

pack of Burgie cans scattered around, and dumps them in the corner behind the couch. Then he stretches out and sleeps.

The first thing he thinks about when he opens his eyes is Wilbur's leg. Was he hooked up good so he could stand right when he was being introduced to Eugene? Benny throws himself off the couch and hurries into the bedroom, but the bed is empty and Wilbur is gone. He looks into Eugene's room and finds it empty. Then he hears the radio playing in the kitchen, and sees Wilbur and old Eugene sitting at the table drinking coffee like they'd known each other for years. Wilbur is sorta slumped in the chair staring into his coffee cup and Eugene's sitting there in his underwear hunched over and inhaling his coffee. The first thing Benny notices when they both look up at him is how much they look alike, mainly around the eyes and mouth, like, if he didn't know better himself, Benny woulda took Wilbur to be old Eugene's son. The second thing he notices is that he didn't get to do what it was he'd set out to do which was to introduce the kid Marine to his old man.

"You're one hell of a host," Eugene says. "Your friend's been up for hours."

"This here's Wilbur," Benny says.

"I know what he's called, goddamit—"

"He's a Marine—"

"I know it. Don't need you to tell me. Knew it the minute I set eyes on him—got the look. Takes one to know one, ain't that right, Marine?"

Wilbur says, "If you say so, sir."

"No need to call me sir. In my day you never called non-coms sir, not even us sarges, even though, if I do say so myself, it was us sarges that run the Corps, not those goddam shavetail ninety day wonders they turned out. Isn't that right, Marine?"

"Un huh," Wilbur says, still staring into his cup, not meeting anybody's eyes, and not caring if the truth was known, his head probably big as a lead balloon from the night before. But Benny's seeing that Eugene's having a good time telling Wilbur all about Guadalcanal and Tarawa and Iwo Jima and how they had to shit in their own foxholes and cook in their helmets if they were lucky enough to have time to build a fire.

"Then we got six days in New Caldonia and bought cheap tail and all the booze we could drink. I had money to burn," he sighs. "Yep. Money to burn. Not that they paid that much in those days, not like today's Corps—right?"

He waits for Wilbur to answer, but Wilbur just seems to slump lower in the chair.

"Right?" old Eugene says again.

Wilbur mumbles something and Eugene bellers, "I can't hear you, Marine!" and Wilbur sits up a little straighter and looks old Eugene right in the eye.

"Where the shit's the goddam booze, Sarge, Sir!" he bellers back into Eugene's stiff face. Then Eugene slams his fist down on the table, sending the coffee cups flying, and Benny, who's leaning against the drainboard listening, gets excited and stands up straight, for he figures this is where his old man's gonna find out what kind of a Marine the kid Wilbur really is, and he's hoping Wilbur will surprise the old man by taking off his leg. But Wilbur hadn't moved a hair, and old Eugene's busting a gut laughing.

"Now that's a Marine! That's a goddam Marine for sure! 'Where the shit's the goddam booze, Sarge, Sir!' he says! Ohgodohgodohgod! Ain't that a goddam Marine? I couldna said it better myself! Hell, yes! Hell, yes! You're right! Where the shit's the goddam booze! Benny! You lazy no–good sonofabitch, get the goddam booze, and don't keep a couple of good men waiting."

Benny picks up the bottle on the drainboard, sees that its empty. "There ain't no more," he says.

"Ain't no more, hell! Look up there in the cupboard, you dumb ox, where I keep my spares, and get us two tall glasses. Me and Wilbur here—what's your rank?—" Wilbur tells him corporal. "Me and the corporal here got us some heavy drinking to do."

Benny rummages in the cupboard, pushes the match box and ketchup aside and knocks the can of Log Cabin syrup out onto the floor. It rattles around and sprays syrup all over old Eugene's bare feet.

"You stupid sonofabitch," he hollers, jumping up, "can't you do one single little thing right?"

"I'm sorry," Benny says.

"Sorry? Sorry? You think that makes it right? All I ask is to do one single little thing like reach into a cupboard and hand me down a bottle of Early Times, and you can't even do that right—"

Benny holds out the bottle. "I said I was sorry—"

"Sorry!" old Eugene groans. "That's all he ever has to say. He's sorry! He's the sorriest goddam sonofabitch I ever seen—"

"Cut the crap, and gimme the goddam bottle," Wilbur says.

"Gimme the goddam bottle!" Eugene says to Benny, grabbing it away. He hands it to Wilbur who cracks the cap and takes a long slug, then pours himself about six fingers in one of the glasses Benny puts on the table. "No Marine ever says he's sorry," Eugene says, watching the way Wilbur chugalugs the glassful of booze like it was beer. "Jesus. Never in my whole life did I say I was sorry. You go through life, you better not be sorry for nothing or nobody, or you'll get your ass kicked by every sonofabitch that thinks maybe he's better'n you." He sits down, fills his glass and drinks, his eyes on Wilbur. "Ain't that right, Marine?"

Wilbur belches and fills his glass. He's not talking and Benny sees it's a race now who can down the second glass first. Wilbur wins hands down and sits there quiet, sliding his thumb up and down on the side of the glass. Then he smiles at old Eugene.

"That's right, Sarge. No Marine ever says he's sorry. I bet you never said you were sorry to anybody in your whole life."

Eugene laughs and grins, fills Wilbur's glass, and shoots Benny a mean look.

"You goddam right! Kick ass or get kicked," he says to Wilbur, "is all I been trying to pound into his thick skull since the day he was born. Even when he was little, before his ma died—she's the one who made him this way! I kept telling her, 'you're makin him into a pansy,' but she did it, anyhow, goddamit, she did—and then here comes Vietnam, and I take him down to Bakersfield to sign him up with the Corps and–and—"

Benny looks down at his bare feet spread out like gunboats on the linoleum so's he won't have to see the real tears in his old man's eyes when he tells Wilbur that Benny got turned down by the Marines for flat feet.

"Flat feet! Look at him! Six foot five and two hunert thirty pounds, and the sonofabitch's got flat feet! I take him to the Navy and the Army and he passes everything again, and they they turn him down—for flat feet! And you know what he says to me?" Eugene's searching Wilbur's face like the kid could change everything if he wanted to. "He says he's sorry! Sorry—"

Wilbur sits there scratching his left hip, not looking at Benny. "Well, war's hell," he says.

"You better believe it," Eugene says, "But it's all we got. What else is there? Here's to the Corps!" He hoists his glass at Wilbur and drains it. "And here's to you, Corporal! I betcha you made your old man proud the day you signed up—I betcha he sat there watching for you on t.v. every night while he was eating his dinner—say! I betcha I seen you on t.v. and didn't even know it! Whaddya think? Huh? Was there t.v. cameras out there where you was fighting? Boy, that's a switch from my day! Never saw no t.v. cameras out there on the Canal. You know why, dontcha? Know why?" Old Eugene is grinning at Wilbur waiting for him to bite on his joke. Wilbur just stares at him. "Didn't even have no t.v. back then, thas why! Ha! Didja ever see a jar full of Jap teeth? Ha! Ha! Ha!" He pours for both of them and hoists his glass again. "Semper Fee–day–lee–US, Corporal! Leave it to the Marines, right, Marine?"

Wilbur drains his glass and slams it on the table. "The Marines suck," he says.

Eugene's mouth falls open. "What?"

"I said fuck the goddam Marines."

Here's where Benny comes to attention. He knows something's going to happen now. He don't know what, but he's hoping it'll include Wilbur's taking off his leg. Old Eugene's face is as red as a fire engine's, and he's breathing hard.

"Don't you never say a thing like that about the Corps," he wheezed.

Then Wilbur giggles. "Fuck the Corps." he says.

Old Eugene stands up and comes charging around the table like a freight train with a drunk engineer. "Who you laughing at? Who you laughing at?" he hollers, and grabs at Wilbur snickering away in the chair, his phony leg stretched out and relaxed. Benny don't know yet exactly what happened next, but he figures Eugene must've tripped on the leg, landing on top of Wilbur, whose hands were doing quick karate chops on his old man's back and neck. By the time Benny got around the table to get a good look the old man was out cold on top of Wilbur.

"Get this sonofabitch off me! I think he's wrecked my goddam leg."

Benny reaches down and lays Eugene out nice and straight on the linoleum. Then he goes over to help Wilbur stand, but Wilbur comes up on his one good leg, his hands cocked for more chopping, and Benny takes one step back. Old Eugene moans but don't move.

"Is it wrecked?" Benny asks.

Wilbur unzips and fiddles with something on his hip, then he flops in the chair and, just like the night before, he whips the plastic leg out the pantleg and stands there checking the joints and the little motor that makes it move.

"Can it be fixed?"

"It's fucked," Wilbur says.

"Holy shit," Benny says.

Wilbur lays the leg on the table and empties the bottle of Early Times into his glass. "Yea, holy shit is right," he says and starts snickering.

"Look," Benny says, "I'm sure sorry—"

"Look," Wilbur says, making his voice low like Benny's, "I'm sure sorry!" Then he collapses on the table, his face next to his plastic leg, and laughs some more. Eugene moans again and Benny sees that the side of his old man's face is laying in the Log Cabin maple syrup. He don't know what to do about Wilbur whose laughing is beginning to sound like he may be crying, so he goes to the sink and gets the dishrag and starts wiping up the syrup and Eugene's face, which looks just about as grey and old as the dishrag. This worries Benny and he kneels down and looks close.

"Pa?"

Old Eugene groans but don't open his eyes.

"Pa? You all right?"

This starts Wilbur, who had quieted down, and he's laughing hardern ever.

"Tell him you're sorry," Wilbur gasps between giggles. "Tell him you're sure sorry you didn't have to shit in your own foxhole! Holy Shit!" He collapses again. "Fox holy shit!"

Eugene twitches and moves an arm. Benny wipes his face again with the syrupy old dishrag. Then he looks at Wilbur who is struggling to get himself up from the table. "What're you gonna do?"

"Get my ass outa here."

"But you can't! Not without that," he says pointing at the leg on the table. "I mean—besides, you don't have a car—I mean, just wait a minute. Lemme get my old man to the couch and I'll drive you back to town." He gets Eugene in his arms and stands.

But Wilbur is hopping out of the kitchen and into the living room. Benny stands there holding Eugene in his arms like a sleeping baby, watching Wilbur go out the door. He hurries to put his old man on the couch and rushes to the table, picks up the leg, hollering, "Hey! You forgot your leg!" When he gets to the door he hears the sound of the engine starting up and Wilbur hollering back, "Fuck the goddam leg!" and when he gets around to the side of the house where the car had been parked he sees his new Mach I burning rubber down the highway.

He stands there holding the leg in the air, watching his car disappear around a bend, then he goes back in the house, and here's Eugene coming to on the couch. He sits up and gives Benny one of his mean looks.

"What kind of a goddam phony SOB—that little bastard—no more a Marine than you are—"

Benny stands there nodding his head. "He's a Marine, all right, Pa," he says and holds out the leg.

"What the hell is that?" old Eugene asks.

And Benny tells him it's Wilbur's plastic leg, and that he'd lost his real one at Khe Sahn, and that Eugene had broke the fake one when he fell on it. Then old Eugene said he was glad, goddamit, that he'd done some damage, the little shit had almost killed him, and don't expect him to be sorry, for he wasn't, he'd find out what a real Marine was, and where the hell was he now?

So Benny tells him that Wilbur had run off on his one good leg and taken Benny's new Mach I, and could he borrow the pickup to go after Wilbur to give him his leg and get the car back, and old Eugene says hell no, he'd be goddamned if he was going to have any part with helping that little shit, or, for that matter, with him, Benny, for what he'd done.

"Please, Pa, just gimme the keys—he's gettin away!"

Old Eugene just crosses his arms and shakes his head. "Do you good losing something—make you pay for what you done to me, bringing a no good little snake like that into my house!"

"Please, Pa, gimme the keys—"

Eugene reaches into his pocket and pulls out his keys. He tosses them in the air, catches them and puts them back where he got them. "Nope. You just learned yourself a lesson you're gonna be sorry for. Ain't that right?"

And this is where Benny tells me he starts swinging at his old man with Wilbur's phony leg, and the rest is ancient history.

Sue Heath Brown

The Uncomplicated Life of Eliot Ozell

Eliot Ozell had led a restrained, uncompulsive, gentle life. He was not going to change now that he was seventy years old and had just buried Esther, his wife of thirty-eight years.

Disciplined in his grief, as in all else, he had made the necessary arrangements, sent the necessary telegrams, and accepted the condolences of his many friends and associates. He had broken down only once.

On the day after the funeral he walked with his two sons on the hillside above their home. Without conscious plan they were holding a memorial service of their own. It was spring, and the grass was that vibrant green that lasts only a little while in California. Everywhere was the cyanotic blue of lupines, which Esther had loved. He and Esther would no longer make their annual pilgrimage down the coast in April to see the bush lupine blowing on the windy slopes above the sea.

Eliot wasn't sure if it was the wild flowers, or the suppressed feelings of his two sons that most affected him. They were trying to be brave for his sake, and he had to turn away from them. Tears filled his eyes and fell so heavily from his face that they left dark splashes on his brown business suit.

"Dad, don't." They came and put their arms around him.

"She'll always be with us," said the youngest.

"Her spirit will never—will never die," choked the eldest, He used to write poetry, but he was a naval architect now.

Eliot could not answer. It seemed to him that their season together, his and Esther's, had been as brief and wonderful as the spring wildflowers. And now there would be no more seasons at all.

When Eliot left his stepfather's house at the age of nineteen, he was grimly determined to make his own way through life's obstacles. He was surprised to find the outside world not half as full of obstacles as he'd expected. For one thing, in this new world, no one told him what to do. But no one needed to. He had been very thoroughly grounded in what was right and what was wrong. Each day he wrote down on a yellow foolscap pad what he was going to accomplish. "Get a job," was what he had written on that first page of foolscap.

He got a job. Impressed with his forthrightness, combined with his diploma from a reputable technical high school, Eliot was hired by the first firm he approached.

Fifteen years later he still wrote methodically on yellow lined paper.

Thirty years later he had switched to legal tablets, and had become the financial vice–president of a large export firm.

In 1930, when he was still only the firm's top accountant, he met in the social hall of St. Timothy's Church, a plain young woman named Esther Clark. He admired her greatly, both for her degree from a woman's college in the midwest, and for her serene, uncomplicated face. She had very bright, healthy skin, clear grayish eyes, and a long, thin nose. Her spare, rangy figure conveyed a sense of integrity and health.

They spent their honeymoon walking in the French Alps. Eliot bought postcards everywhere. They were pictures of what they'd seen together—mountain peaks named Les Fiz and Col de Plate, sturdy chalets with rocks on their roofs, green meadows full of glossy brown cows.

Esther and he then settled down to rear their family of boys. Due to her upbringing, a strict one like his own, they had both experienced a certain restraint in their physical intimacy. However, their total relationship was one of such deep and abiding affection that it would have flourished if there had been no physical contact at all. Esther was a rarity even in her own day—completely happy in her role of wife and mother. Her primary passion was to make a home for Eliot and to raise their children. Surplus energy and joy spilled over into gardening, church work, and the taking in of destitute cousins and homeless students. The rambling stone house near the campus of a large university was always full of people.

Marian and Ross Williams were one of the earliest young–marrieds to find a temporary home with the Ozells. Ross was a physics instructor. Esther and Eliot's boys were half grown by this time. Marian was very good with them and let them play with her own infant son as if he were a doll; she seemed to have complete confidence that they would not hurt him. Both Williams were unusual people, with strong beliefs in the essential goodness of man. In spite of the fifteen–year difference in their ages, Marian and Esther became fast friends. Eliot was as fond of Marian as if she were an older daughter. The Ozells were sorry when the Williams finally saved enough money to move into a house of their own.

As they moved into middle age together, Esther's figure grew more spare and her hair turned a brisk gray. Her nose became finer and more delicate, and her nature grew more serene and lovely. Eliot was still so infatuated with her that he could not keep his arm from going around her waist whenever she was near him. However, his was not a compulsive love. Neither was it complicated by the charms of other women younger and more attractive than Esther. He had had the same secretary for almost twenty years; she had been young and pretty when she first came to work for him, and Eliot assumed she had not changed. He was a very happy man in his work, and his ten–hour days, with the commute to the city, kept half his life completely separate from Esther. Yet he felt securely enclosed by his family, like a good sturdy frame around a favorite picture. Each night when he came home, he rediscovered the picture inside the frame, and it was a wonder and a delight all over again. The time went by so swiftly that Eliot hardly realized when one year ended and another began. Esther never seemed to grow any older. But one day Eliot was shocked to notice that his young secretary's hair had turned gray.

His sons left high school, turned into fine young men, and went away to graduate schools and then into businesses and marriages.

More alone now than he'd ever been in his life, even in his childhood, Eliot felt the frame of his life had come apart and allowed the picture to drop out and become lost. He found himself often unable to sleep at night.

"I think it's being alone in the house," he admitted to Marian when she came to see him. "I'll get used to it in time."

But he didn't, and after a few months, he moved into the first apartment he went to see, a white–walled place like a series of hospital rooms. Even with some of the familiar furniture in it, the place remained alien. To avoid coming back to it, he would stay in a hotel in the city. On the nights when he did return to the campus town, he rewarded himself first with a visit to the Williams.

When Marian Williams realized that Eliot was not really living in his apartment, she took him in hand, went with him to buy drapes, arranged to have the walls painted a warmer color, and made him lay in a stock of groceries.

"You must eat breakfast," she admonished. "You can have dinner with us, but breakfast in your own place." She spoke sternly, like a mother to her child. Then, seeing his meek look, softened her voice to "Oh Eliot!" and gave him a hug which made his ribs crack. She was a tall, strong, intense woman, with honey–colored hair worn in a braid around her head. Eliot wondered why he'd never noticed before that she had the same direct blue–gray eyes that Esther had had. But there the resemblance ended, for Marian had two *verrucus papula* on her chin, which she and everyone else ignored, partly because of her Christian Science, but mainly because she carried her head and shoulders so erect that people thought what a handsome woman she was. She was also so warm and outgoing that each person felt immediately drawn into a private circle of friendship with her.

Eliot began, if not to live in his refurbished apartment, at least to feel that it was where he belonged. Yet he spent as much time as ever away. He did a good deal of traveling about the country.

One evening in New York City he met a good–looking woman at a dinner party. Her name was Belva Didier. She was a teacher of music at a woman's college in Westchester County and a competent, if not an excellent, pianist. After dinner she performed some diffident Schumann etudes. Eliot found her white arms and lightly clothed bosom charming. It was hard to tell her age. Would she be the age of Esther? He didn't know. Belva invited him to visit her apartment when next he came to town. And he did. She lived with her mother, an aristocratic little person, who was quite deaf. The apartment was elegantly furnished, with an old Bechstein in the corner of the living room. It reminded Eliot vaguely of his home when Esther was alive. Eliot expected all women to be good cooks. And Belva was a ravishing cook. With poached salmon and souffled potatoes under his belt, he found Belva particularly attractive. Her white arms against the dark velvet couch she sat on were irresistible. He touched them, at first tentative, but then with real ardor.

When he left to go back to his hotel, Belva twittered over him. "Now, Eliot, you must feel you have a home here, whenever you come east."

"Thank you," he said, and pressed her forearm lightly.

On the west coast he thought of her with gratitude.

Months went by, even a year. He made increasingly frequent trips to New York. Most of these trips he could have assigned to younger men in his department, but he liked going to New York because there he was spoiled by Belva and her mother. In his own apartment in California, he would imagine Belva sitting on his chintz covered couch—and realized the couch was not really elegant enough for her; it would have to be re–covered. There had been too many launderings, boys' rough–housing, and—yes—even love–makings on that couch. It depressed him. How could his life have become so empty?

He felt much more at home on Belva's velvet settee. Except for the presence of her mother. She reminded Eliot of a sharp little predatory bird. Being deaf, she did not enter into conversations very often, but perched in corners doing needlework. When she did speak, her pronouncements had an oracular authority.

"Belva," she announced to Eliot on one of his earliest visits, "Is an unusual woman. She has never required the attentions of men."

Eliot was a little taken aback. But he agreed with her politely.

"She has always put her musical career ahead of marriage."

Again Eliot agreed with her, though wondering privately what kind of musical career she could have while teaching in a small woman's college. He was a little afraid of Belva's mother. He felt they were talking about someone he didn't know, rather than the real Belva—who was standing right there, dressed in an evening gown, waiting for him to take her to a concert.

"Don't pay any attention to Mama," she said, as they left the apartment. She blushed slightly. "She thinks I'm still a little girl."

Eliot squeezed her arm. "I'd say you are very much a grown woman. A beautiful woman."

"Oh Eliot," she giggled.

After the concert they came quietly into the darkened apartment. Belva poured them each a glass of the wine left from dinner. It was an excellent Gewürztraminer, not too sweet.

"I think Mama's gone to bed," said Belva after they'd clinked around in the kitchen for a while, pouring more wine, getting cheese and crackers. Eliot thought she sounded relieved. "Let's go on into the living room."

Warmed by the wine, Eliot found himself, quite unintentionally, putting his arm about her and very gently (for he was a gentle man) exploring her breasts. He supposed it was because she'd been wearing an evening gown which didn't quite stay together in front. She had been fidgeting with it all evening, as if it had made her nervous too. Now she giggled like a girl and only half slapped at his hand. He clasped the hand and kissed her on the mouth. Her lips quivered uncertainly. Good heavens, hadn't she ever been kissed before?

One thing led to another. He was very cautious, very gradual. She seemed to like what he was doing and did not check him. He was surprised afterwards. Esther, when he'd been courting her, had been very prim and proper.

Now Belva began to write to him. She had not done that before. She told him what a nice person Mama had said he was, and that she hoped they would see him again soon. "I shall miss you," Belva ended the letter.

Although Eliot recalled with pleasure his evening in Belva's apartment, he did not really miss her. He had fallen back into his routine of having dinner twice a week with the Williams. He was taking an interest in their boys, younger than his own, and still at home. Ross Williams was a tall, silent, rugged man in his forties, who thought constantly about physics. He did not have Marian's instantaneous warmth. His personality, strong and sweet in its own way, was more hidden. When they came together, Marian and Ross, they would reach toward each other with their hands or their eyes, no matter who else was there. When Eliot was present, this shook his heart with a sharp, familiar sensation.

When he played cribbage with one of the boys, Marian often came near to watch. Eliot would put his arm around her aproned waist and squeeze gently. Yet it made him feel sad again, as a child is sad who has lost his real mother and now has only a kind stepmother. Indeed, Marian Williams treated him as a child, with all the affection and gentleness she had in such abundance. Eliot drove away from their home in the evenings feeling both comforted and forlorn.

He had begun going on trips for his firm mainly to avoid being alone in his apartment, and to fill in the times when he couldn't be with the Williams. Now there were partings from Belva as well as from Marian. But it was of Marian that he thought most obsessively. As soon as the plane took off he would start thinking what gift he could take back to her that would bring the quick jump of joy to her face; he would anticipate the moment when Marian would exclaim, "Oh Eliot, you shouldn't have!" And then the inevitable hug, which always stabbed him with little–boy bashfulness, so that he even blushed. Ross would look at him curiously but say nothing.

A time came when Eliot realized he must make a business trip abroad. He knew he would be near the scenes of his honeymoon trip with Esther. He remembered all too vividly the joy they had discovered in each other and in the spectacular scenery at Le Fayet. At first, he was happy to think he could go and see those places again. Then he remembered he would not have Esther's smooth hand in his, or her eyes seeing the mountains with him. A dread rushed over him of even setting foot in the same country without her. Of course, he could go and simply stay in Paris? That would be safe.

He was not a neurotic or a morbid person, but suddenly he felt immobilized, not even able to buy the tickets or make the other necessary arrangements.

"When are you going?" Marian would ask gaily whenever he saw her. She was genuinely glad that he was undertaking this European trip. To her, any trip meant enjoyment. She refused to see his indecision.

Finally he mumbled to her, "I don't think I'll go, after all."

"What?" she cried. "Why ever not?"

He couldn't look at her. He felt almost like weeping.

"If—if—" For the first time in his life he was stuttering. "If—" He was speaking so low she could barely hear him. "If you would go with me, I might still go."

"Oh Eliot, don't be silly. How could I go? I can't afford it. And leave Ross? What a crazy idea!"

To Eliot it did not seem crazy at all. Now that he had actually said it.

"I would pay for your trip," he stated, watching her face. "I can afford it."

"Oh Eliot! It's crazy!" But her eyes danced with excitement. "Oh I wish I *could*."

"Why can't you then?"

"But Eliot, I couldn't let you! What about Ross?" He could see she was tempted.

"Ross can go too," Eliot said, taking the chance, but feeling, all of a sudden, very daring, very brave.

Marian stared at him curiously for a moment. "Eliot, what is the matter?"

"Nothing, I just don't want to go alone." His voice was as deliberate and as unemotional as he could make it.

"You mean, Esther?"

"Yes…And other reasons."

Marian did not ask him what the other reasons were.

"Oh, it would be such fun!" she cried.

"Why don't you ask Ross?"

"Right now?"

"Why not?"

Eliot listened as she telephoned Ross at his laboratory. With a pang, Eliot heard the other softness enter her voice as her husband came on the line. She told him, all in a rush, like a child telling a secret.

She received Ross's response as if it were an electric shock. Her whole body went taut with joy. "Oh Ross, do you really think so...? But why can't *you*—? Yes, I know (here her long waist sagged in the chair)...all right. We'll talk about it later... Goodbye, dear."

She turned to Eliot. "He thinks it's a wonderful idea! But he doesn't think he can take that much time away. He thinks *I* should go if I want to... Oh Eliot, do you think he means that?"

Her naivete moved him. He tried to be honest. "Well, knowing Ross, I don't think he would say that unless he meant it, do you?"

"No–o, I guess not." Marian was thoughtful.

In the ensuing weeks of discussion and preparation she never once said what any other woman would have said: "What will people think?" Ross took them to the airport. Eliot watched almost objectively as Ross and Marian embraced. They were both tall and could look straight into each other's faces without peering up or down.

Beautiful people, thought Eliot. But Marian, with her taffy hair in a snake's coil on top of her head, was the most beautiful.

Eliot kept his thoughts from racing ahead. He had made the reservations with care. He and Marian would have, whenever possible, adjoining rooms. For the first time since Esther died, he was conscious of an intense inner pleasure.

When they changed planes in New York he thought of telephoning Belva. An obscure sense of duty shirked troubled him when he did not.

Marian had never been to Europe. The smallest things delighted her, from the old women in the flower stalls to the men urinating with such unconcern against the walls of ancient houses. Even the sour–faced ticket takers on the Parisian streetcars responded to her joyful, ungrammatic French, and smiled at her. At night they walked along the Seine in a chill wind and Marian tried to peer into the sordid houseboats. Eliot took her hand and put it into his coat pocket along with his.

"I should have brought a warmer coat," she laughed. He bought her a long bright wool scarf which she wound around her neck and head, hiding her heavy shining hair, which was just as well, as he found himself frantic to stroke it.

It was not until they reached the village of Le Fayet that Eliot forgot himself. All the way up on the little funicular he had been besieged by memories. His own youth, the shyness and simplicity of his new bride—now dead—all came back to excite him. His eyes shone and his long, serious face became boyish as he pointed out to Marian where he and Esther had walked, up this peak, or that valley, and picked crocuses from snowbanks.

"Oh Eliot, I'm so glad you had that happy time with Esther," exclaimed Marian. "Whatever happens, nothing will change that."

Eliot had to look away because he was afraid he would weep. Though whether it was for the past or the present, it was hard to know.

That night they stood on the upper balcony of the Gasthous and looked out into the moonlight glinting on nearby peaks. There was the rich smell of damp earth and flowers blooming in the dark, and the dissonant sound of cowbells.

"Marian," Eliot said. He clasped her to him tightly. "I'm so fond of you! Can't you—can you—love me just a little?"

Marian let him hold her for a moment. Then she moved out of his arms gently. "Eliot, of course I love you. You know that." She touched his face with her fingers. "But not in that way." She peered at him to see the face she'd touched. Then impulsively kissed a cheek. "Oh Eliot. There are all kinds of love."

"Yes. I suppose so." He kept his voice expressionless.

"I don't like to hurt you, my dear. You are so very sweet. I love you *dearly*. But," she hesitated, "You know how I love Ross?"

He was ashamed to attack such forthrightness, but the strength of his feeling carried him on. "Ross would never know," he suggested softly. "Perhaps he might not care—if he didn't know?"

"Eliot, you know better than that." It was Esther's way of rebuking him, gentle but firm.

"Yes," said Eliot, giving up. But he put his arm about her waist and squeezed strongly, as he used to do with Esther.

On the plane back from France, Eliot told Marian about Belva. As he tried to describe Belva, without disclosing the physical attraction she had exerted on him,, his words became stilted and a little confused. Marian's eyes searched his face.

"I don't understand, Eliot," she said gently, "What are you trying to say?"

"I—I don't know."

"Oh, I think you know." She waited. When he didn't proceed, she said, "You want to be married again, and you're thinking of Belva. You're thinking that Belva can take Esther's place."

Eliot flinched from the direct gray eyes. "Yes. I suppose so."

"I think that's wonderful!" said Marian decisively. Her enthusiasm jetted over Eliot like healing balm. He felt safe again.

To Eliot's surprise, when they walked off the plane, there were his two sons waiting for them. He was glad to see Ross there as well. It seemed to him that Marian's embrace of her husband was more exuberant than usual, even for her. Perhaps she felt the same awkwardness as he did. As for Ross, he asked no questions, gave no searching looks. His face was gravely happy as he gazed into Marian's face.

Disengaging herself from Ross finally, Marian shook hands with Eliot's sons, saying, "How nice of you to meet us!"

"Why didn't you tell us you were going to France?" said the oldest son.

"We got your postcards," said the youngest. "We had to come up to the city anyhow, so we thought we'd meet you. We called Ross to find out what plane you'd be on." His voice, like his brother's, was a shade accusatory.

"May we give 'you a lift?" asked the oldest one politely to Ross and Marian.

"I have my car," said Ross, "Thank you."

"Well, we can take Dad home, then."

It was strange to Eliot being with his two sons in the car. He'd almost forgotten that he had two grown sons. He'd been with Marian so constantly that now he felt her sudden absence like a physical pain. He'd hardly had a chance to say goodbye to her.

The oldest son, the naval architect, driving, glanced at him. "Did you have a good time in France?" There was an ironic inflection to his words.

"Yes. Yes, I did," said his father, judiciously. He felt a little dazed from the long jet trip.

"Really, Dad," murmured his other son from the back seat.

Eliot wasn't sure he'd heard him correctly. He began to ask him about his two small children.

The sons stayed with Eliot in his apartment overnight. The next morning the oldest saw fit to speak with him further. Eliot was getting ready to catch his train to the city.

"Dad, that was rather unwise, don't you think? Taking Marian off to Europe with you like that."

"I don't see anything wrong in it," replied his father, with some acerbity. "I'm very fond of Marian, and she's never been to Europe."

"Yes, I know, but everyone thinks it's a bit much."

"Everyone? Who is everyone?"

"Well, I mean us, the family."

Eliot looked hard at his son. "Marian used to put band–aids on your knees when you were a youngster. And stay with you when Esther and I went on trips. We've known Marian and Ross for almost twenty years; they are my oldest friends."

"I *know*, Dad, but—"

"I don't want to hear any more of this nonsense!" Eliot felt himself trembling. He supposed he was upset. He very seldom was upset. He added, "Since you are taking such an interest in my affairs, I suppose I'd better tell that I am going away again in a few days."

"Dad, I think you buzz around too much. After all, you're seventy–three now, or is it seventy–four?"

"As I was saying," Eliot was not able to smile, "I am going to New York. There is a lovely lady there, named Belva Didier. I believe I shall ask her to marry me."

His sons' astonished reaction was gratifying. And aggravating.

"Dad! Why didn't you tell us?"

"Dad, you're not going to get married again, at your age?"

When he flew back to New York and asked Belva to marry him, she accepted with alacrity. Being a pious woman, as well as a woman who had suppressed her physical needs for years, she had wondered what her punishment would be.

She found out soon enough. It was Eliot who was both her reward and her punishment.

The wedding was in California. At the reception Belva was introduced to the Williams. Ross was formal and enigmatic. But Marian had just given Eliot such a bone cracking embrace that Belva was alarmed. She drew back, fearing the same treatment. But Marian seemed to sense Belva's reserve, and contented herself with grasping Belva's hand in both her strong ones. Belva feared for her pianist fingers, and disengaged them as soon as she could. As the Williams passed down the receiving line and out of earshot, Belva's mother hissed into her ear, "I don't like that woman. She looks wicked."

"Oh Mama," soothed Belva. "They are Eliot's oldest friends."

"Friends?" sniffed her mother, and went to sit down in a corner away from the press of people, most of whom she disapproved. Westerners, she thought, seemed completely lacking in the social niceties.

Belva respected her mother's judgment in almost everything. So she kept a wary eye on Marian Williams; she certainly seemed to enjoy hugging people, both men and women. She couldn't imagine ever becoming a friend of hers. But that was what Eliot had said: "You and Marian will be good friends, I know."

Belva found more in common with the young wives of Eliot's sons. They had helped her in so many ways. One had come to help her unpack. The other had taken her shopping for towels and kitchen utensils, which Eliot's apartment had sadly lacked.

"Where are you going on your honeymoon?" asked the oldest son's wife, adding, "You don't have to tell me if you don't want to." She was the daughter of a banker, and Belva liked her immediately.

"Why, Eliot is taking me to a place on the coast called Carmel. He says it's nicer than the Riviera."

"Hmm," said the wife. "So he's not taking you to France?"

"Oh no. That's much too far. And expensive."

"—and of course he's just had a trip there," added the young woman.

"Oh? I didn't know that. He didn't tell me."

"I shouldn't think he would tell you." The young wife laughed in an odd, insinuating way.

"Whatever do you mean?" Belva was genuinely puzzled.

"Oh nothing. You'd better ask Eliot."

Eliot had continued his friendship with the Williams. He was not a man who changed his habits or his feelings easily. He even continued his luncheons with Marian in the city. When the sons got wind of this, they told their wives. Their wives casually mentioned it to Belva.

Belva had been brought up in a milieu where men did not lunch alone with other men's wives. Still, she was more puzzled than alarmed. When she asked Eliot, he readily admitted taking Marian to lunch, and suggested that Belva join them the next time. Then Belva remembered what her daughter–in–law had said, and asked Eliot if he had been to Europe, and whether the Williams had gone too?

Eliot was a little hesitant in his reply. Finally he said, "I suppose I should have told you. But at the time it didn't seem to have anything to do with *us*." He tried to clasp Belva to him, but she stood away from him and asked angrily, "What do you mean?"

"Well, my dear, I—Ross couldn't go. It was just Marian who went. I suppose people jumped to conclusions. Which were completely unwarranted." Seeing Belva's look, he added, "Have you been listening to someone's gossip?" When she didn't answer, he went on firmly, "There was nothing between Marian and me. If you knew Marian, you'd know this... I hope that you *will* get to know her."

"Why," gasped Belva, "I'll do no such thing. I don't want to get to know her. I don't even want to see her again. And I expect you to do the same!"

"But, my dear—"

"Don't even mention her name to me; I don't want to hear about her!" With surprise, Eliot saw tears on her face as she ran past him out of the room.

Belva had been a reserved, mild–mannered, almost spinsterish woman, who lived for her music and her mother—until Eliot came along. She'd even suffered some honest, old–fashioned guilt over her relations with Eliot. Now she thought to herself, why should I feel guilty when he's no better than an—an adulterer. But she brooded. She talked to her daughters–in–law, who seemed to sympathize (perhaps they worried about their husbands following in their father's footsteps?) They told her that Eliot was still seeing Marian.

"Oh," cried Belva, wounded anew. "She's horrible. How can she do this to me?"

"Oh, she's a nice enough person," the daughters–in–law said, a little uncomfortable. "She just leads Dad on. It's the way she is."

That was enough for Belva. Overnight she became possessed by a jealous outrage, bordering on fury.

The first time Eliot came home and heard her voice at an unfamiliar pitch, the accusations pouring from her mouth like obscenities, he put it down to menopausal tantrum. In all their years of marriage, Esther had never shouted. But then neither had Esther been given to sexual abandon. Eliot had been quite pleased to find his second wife such a passionate woman. It compensated for a number of things.

However, now he found himself the object of jealous scorn instead of passion.

"I'll never let you touch me as long as you see that Williams woman. Never!" screeched Belva, slamming the door of their bedroom shut behind her. She had not, Eliot noticed next, even cooked dinner. He did not remonstrate, judging she was in no fit mood for reasonable discussion. He fixed himself some eggs, and went to sleep in the den.

Over a period of weeks, Belva did not relent. Eliot tried to reason with her. "Marian was Esther's friend, and mine, for seventeen years," he explained. "I don't want to hurt her..."

"You don't want to hurt *her*? What about me?"

"I don't want to hurt you either." Eliot had never noticed before how Belva's eyes protruded when she was upset. She looked positively dangerous. He wanted only to live in peace and harmony. He said, "If it means so much to you, I will not see Marian any more."

Belva continued to glare at him. "Do you promise not to see her again?"

"Yes. I will not see her or speak to her, if that's what you want."

"It is."

As soon as he could, Eliot telephoned Marian and told her he would not be able to see her for a while.

"Oh, I understand," she cried. "You and Belva need time for yourselves. I'm so happy for you two!"

"Yes,"" agreed Eliot. But his voice, even to him, sounded as though it were strained through thick porridge. "Goodbye," he said.

Eliot kept his promise to Belva. He was an honorable man. However, it was as if his giving up of Marian acted as some kind of admission of guilt. Belva became more and more inflamed. She refused to believe that he did not see Marian. She questioned his sons and their wives when they came to visit, and even his office staff. Did he make any telephone calls? Did he go to lunch early or late? What time did he leave the office?

To escape her inquisitions, Eliot came home later, and took an earlier train in the mornings while Belva still slept.

Belva stopped playing the piano and moped about the apartment. Finally she sent for her mother, who had gone back to New York immediately after the wedding. At least, Belva thought, her mother could keep her company. Eliot was so seldom home. Eliot hoped the mother would somehow bring Belva and him together again. But Belva repulsed him as vigorously as before, and her mother watched him like a miniature bird of prey. He took to staying one or two nights a week in the city. Belva would telephone him late at night at his club, to make sure he was there. During this period Eliot still did not visit the Williams, or even telephone to them. He held on to the belief that his loyalty and his word of honor would be believed and that he would be reinstated in his new wife's heart and home. It did not happen.

In this interval, Eliot retired for the second time and was honored at a reception and formal dinner. Belva attended with him. She liked social affairs and liked wearing her tasteful, expensive clothes. Eliot enjoyed having her at his side, in spite of the fact that she spoke to him as little as possible. She was, he thought, a fine figure of a woman. In spite of her sixty years she was still slim, aristocratic, high breasted, with the trimmest ankles he'd ever seen. She ignored him. Yet when he talked to other women, her eyes registered it. Once he heard her say archly, "Oh Eliot likes the ladies."

It was the kind of remark Esther would never have made.

When they went home, rather keyed up from the successful evening (a number of speeches had been made in Eliot's honor), Eliot thought he detected a softening in Belva's manner toward him. He cupped his hands around her small waist and tried to pull her to him.

"No, no," she cried in artificial horror, as if she were a newly–minted virgin. "Oh no. Don't you put your hands on me when you are still seeing *her*."

Eliot could hardly believe his ears. "But I'm *not* seeing her. Belva, I've told you, I have not seen nor spoken to the Williams for more than four months." Desperately, he added, "What more do you expect me to do?"

"I don't believe you," she stated flatly. Then she left the room. Eliot could hear her voice, raised so her mother could hear her; they were talking about something completely inconsequential.

A fissure of anger opened in him at last. Well, then. Never in all his life had his honesty and integrity been questioned—not just questioned, insulted! Eliot felt a sense of absolution. He was free. Belva herself had absolved him.

The next morning he mailed Marian a card showing the alpine peaks known as Les Fiz. The postcard was a little brown with age, but it performed its function. Two days later Eliot telephoned and asked Marian to lunch with him.

"Oh Eliot," she cried. I don't remember you buying that postcard?"

He explained, with his usual exactitude, that he bought it forty–two years ago, when he was with Esther.

The waiters in the old Italian restaurant were white–haired and world weary. They knew about human folly and respected it. Like solicitous shadows they hovered in the dimness around Eliot and Marian. The snowy tablecloth hung in generous folds and Eliot was able to place his hand invisibly upon Marian's.

He told her all he'd been through with Belva.

Marian gave him her complete attention. When he finished, she had tears in her eyes. "You've been treated abominably," she cried. It was characteristic of her that she did not criticize Belva more than that.

Eliot now lifted her hand above the table and pressed it to his mouth, caressing the fingers with his lips.

In a low, embarrassed voice, he said, "I've been dreadfully lonely. Belva won't let me even—I mean, I can't even—"

Marian gave a start of indignation, but did not withdraw her fingers.

"Eliot, what are you saying?"

"It's true," mourned Eliot.

Marian's eyes hardened. Eliot had never seen Marian angry. It made him dizzy with emotion. His emotion, and hers, seemed to form a current between them.

Marian stared down at their hands in a puzzled, unseeing way. Her face, usually so agile, was constrained.

"Eliot," she murmured. "You mustn't suffer because of—because of –me."

"I'm not suffering," said Eliot, quite honest. "I'm not suffering now."

Marian sat so still that Eliot could hear her breath coming unevenly. She stared at their hands, locked on the tablecloth. His hands were not those of an old man at all; the skin was still taut, the knuckles undeformed. Together, their hands made a shocking, rather livid lump upon the too white cloth.

"Oh dear," she murmured once.

"I'm so fond of you," he whispered.

"I'm fond of you too. I've always been fond of you."

Marian took him up again into her life. Not quite as she'd done before, when he'd lost Esther, but with a new wholeness which mended his spirit. Eliot saw her regularly, on the days he went to his club. Once again he stopped at the Williams' house on his way home. Ross was as friendly as ever, and as incurious. Eliot made no attempt at dissimulation. He was as restrained and proper as he'd always been. Indeed, his life didn't seem much changed. Except for Belva.

Belva could not hold out against Eliot's restraint. The strength of his patience was greater than her anger. Her jealous behavior disappeared as if it had never existed. She began to play the piano again. Eliot would sit in his favorite wing chair after dinner while she played a Mozart sonata, or a Schubert song, often accompanying herself in a light contralto that Eliot found charming.

He felt his life grow smooth and uncomplicated once more.

Belva flew into a frenzy of redecorating. Unwittingly, she discarded all the colors picked out by Marian several years before. She went further, persuading Eliot to get rid of most of the heavy furniture that had been Esther's and his. Belva substituted fragile Chippendale for the weighty mahogany. Eliot thought the graceful, spindle-shanked tables and chairs bore a remarkable resemblance to Belva's own slim legs and ankles.

Belva found her mother a separate apartment in the same building, so that now she and Eliot could spend their evenings alone together, as they had done before their marriage. Marian's name was never mentioned. Eliot was careful to call her only from pay telephones.

On his 84th birthday Belva gave a large party for Eliot. His sons came with their families. The festivities lasted from afternoon until well into the evening. So many people made Eliot feel rather tired. He looked forward to the next day, which would be his usual day with Marian.

He lunched with Marian in the city at their usual restaurant. She had brought him a tiny nosegay of yellow rosebuds embedded in a spray of forget–me–nots. She kissed him as she put it in his lapel.

"Do you think she'll mind?" she murmured.

"I'll tell her I bought it myself, from a poor old blind woman." Eliot took one of Marian's hands and kissed it.

Their lunch lasted longer than usual, almost three hours. Eliot drank most of the bottle of Beaulieu Cabernet'49, and they sipped innumerable small cups of Italian coffee.

It was after four o'clock when Eliot said, regretfully, "I'll get caught in the commuter traffic."

"Oh yes, you must go. I didn't realize it was so late!" Marian leaped up. "I'll drive you to the station."

Eliot was home in plenty of time for dinner. Belva had prepared an excellent meal, for which Eliot had less appetite than usual. There were candles still on the table from his birthday party, and a centerpiece of grape hyacinths. Their intense color stabbed Eliot's memory—they were like the lupines Esther had loved. For a moment he thought he saw Esther standing in the doorway. He jumped from his chair—and saw that it was Belva.

"Beautiful," he murmured, as he kissed her. He sat down again.

"Where did you get the boutonniere?" asked Belva.

"I bought it from a blind woman. She was selling flowers on the corner when I came out of the club."

Belva nodded and came around the table to serve him the broiled salmon. Eliot noticed that she was wearing the dusky voile dress he liked so much. It set off the whiteness of her bare arms and shoulders.

When they finished their creme caramel and coffee, she asked, "Shall I play for you?"

"Yes, I'd like that."

Belva began to sing Schumann's Widmung. It was one of Eliot's favorites. *"Du mein Welt, in wer ich lebe..."* The lovely song rang out strong and clear at first, *"Du hebst mich liebend under mich..."* But why was Belva dropping her voice? The words seem to fade and become faint in Eliot's ears. He thought this strange, as his hearing had never been impaired. He tried to sit forward in his chair, straining to hear, but found he could not move. Then the outlines of Belva's body became indistinct, and there was Esther in Belva's place. It was startling but not frightening. Belva's body reappeared and Esther was gone. The music, which had faded, became audible again. Eliot felt as though he were peering into a camera trying to refocus the lens. His heart, which had never varied in its rhythms, suddenly felt too full, and beat heavily as if he were running uphill. He took several deep breaths to give his happiness room to expand. He felt his pulse hammering, and then, suddenly, the blood ebbing away to distant parts of his body—just as the melody ebbed away. The words grew more and more faint, but it didn't matter, for he knew them by heart:

"Lift me, loving, above all else,
My good spirit, my better self..."

Sue Heath Brown

The Moon Snail

The moon snail slides
from the sea, bearing
a fruited dome of shell,
an apple-peeling home.
It leaves barely
a ribbon—
a minor chord
to giant sea lions
who sloughed their shells
aeons of time ago
and now leave only
fleshly, obscene
trails upon the sand.
Under the moon,
their frailer kin,
the moon snail,
knits its crèche of eggs
and spits them there
above the tidal lip.
Then, hours upon hours,
labors to construct
a sepulcher so thin
it would not bury
Polinices.
Fragile, yes,
yet spun so strong
of sand and salt
and sessile mucous,
it guards
in tiny mosques
its sunken treasure:

millions of crystal roe,
millions of lunar heroes
to be born, to slide
their own slow
ways to sea.

Mary H. McLaughlin

The Spring Well

We crossed the white stile
to the field of St. Bridget's Well,
the tin pail swinging
between us.

With caution we approached
the threatening hawthorn bush
that half concealed the spring
and fully hid the little folk
who practiced mischief as an art.
Humbly we dipped our pail
to draw our mortal share
of precious water:
then scampered home
through the twilight,
a Celtic Jack and Jill
pursued by phantoms.

Mary H. McLaughlin
Three Irish Tales

The Wanderer

A s she sat on the top step tying her shoelaces, Moira could hear her father's voice down in the kitchen. It was raised above his normal tone and she wondered if he could be having an early morning argument with Granda. She hoped not. Granda was Mama's father and Mama got upset when the two argued.

"He's an old man, Mike, and he misses my mother," she would say, trying to excuse her father's frequent outbursts of ill temper.

Moira listened more carefully, and then she could make out the words.

"She's as proud of me as an old hen that has a duck for a chicken."

That was Conn, the Shaughraun. She remembered suddenly. Tonight was the play and they were going to let her stay up late, so that she could see her father play Conn. He and some of his friends had formed an amateur theatrical group in the village and tonight was the big night. A year ago they had done "The Colleen Bawn," but she had been too young to go. Now she was almost seven and watched and listened to her father as he stood shaving in front of the looking–glass that hung on the wall in the kitchen, while he rehearsed Conn's lines. She knew a lot of them by heart from having heard them so often. She listened again.

"Hould your whist now. Wipe your mouth and give us a kiss."

That was Conn talking to his sweetheart Moya. She could picture Dada sharpening his long straight razor on the leather razor strop, as he spoke the words into the mirror, pulling his shoulders back and raising himself to seem a little taller. He did not like being a trifle shorter than Mama and was always trying to stretch himself an inch when he got close to her.

"Moira, is that you up there? Come on down and help me with the breakfast." It was her mother's voice calling and Moira jumped up and hurried down the curving wooden staircase to the kitchen.

Her mother was stirring the pot of oatmeal stirabout that hung over the hearth fire and her father was by the window, staring in the looking glass as she had pictured him. The script of the play was open on the window ledge, and he glanced at it now and then.

"What do you want me to do, Mama?" Moira asked.

"Just get the baby out from under my feet and I'll do the rest," said her mother.

Moira made a dive at Baby Mickey, who scurried under the table, but she ran around the other side and pulled him out, standing him on his feet as she held both his arms and walked behind him. She was trying to teach him to walk, but at eleven months, he found crawling a much faster method of getting from one place to another. It was Moira's job to keep him out of danger and see that he did not put strange things in his mouth. He had a small piece of coal in his fist now and she took it from him and threw it in the fire.

"Come, Mickey. Let's go and watch Dada shaving."

She propped him up on the window seat and sat beside him.

"Do you know all the lines now, Dada?" she asked.

"I know Conn's part forwards and backwards. What I'm worried about is some of the cast will forget theirs and give me the wrong cues."

She suspected sometimes that her father would like to be able to play all the parts. He could sing, "Where are you going to, my pretty maiden?" in the soft voice of Claire Ffoliott, who was pretending to be a milkmaid in the opening scene. Then he could drop his voice to a thunderous roar as Harvey Duff with the lines,

"If there is justice in Heaven, you and I will meet again on this side of the grave. Have your soul ready."

"What does Shaughraun mean, Dada?" Moira asked. He had told her that once before, but she enjoyed his lectures about the theatre as much as he enjoyed giving them.

"Didn't I tell you that weeks ago? The Shaughraun is a Gaelic word meaning 'the Wanderer'. The play was first performed in New York in 1874, and Boucicault himself played Conn. He was a playwright, actor and manager."

The way he said it Moira knew he would like to be Boucicault instead of working at the Department of Agriculture.

"Are you going to wear costumes?"

"Of course. We have them up at the school hall. You'll see them tonight if you don't fall asleep before the play starts."

Her father put his razor down on the shelf under the looking glass and Mickey, who had been wriggling in Moira's tight grasp while they talked, reached eagerly for the shiny weapon, but Moira pulled him away before he could touch it.

Her mother called, "Come on, Mike, and have breakfast before the other children come downstairs, and be sure to put that razor out of harm's way."

"Where's the ould fella, this mornin?" asked Mike as he sat down at the table and poured milk over his porridge.

"He went down the back garden for a bit of a daunder. I hope he stays out till you've finished eating. I'm in no mood to hear the two of you at it this mornin'," said Mama.

"Now Ellen, he's always the one to start it. Even if it is his house, I'm paying our way. I don't have to put up with his growling."

"He's not a well man, Mike. It's hard on him to be old and not be able to till the land like he used to. Shush now, I hear him comin'. Not a word out of you."

The back door opened and with a great deal of shuffling and coughing Granda came in, shooshing at the hens who tried to follow him into the warm kitchen.

"Come over to the fire, Father, and I'll fix you a bowl of stirabout," said Ellen, pulling out the wicker armchair near the hearth.

"Isn't there a place for me at me own table?" growled the old man.

"Sure there is, if you want it. I thought you'd rather be closer to the fire." Ellen patted the kitchen chair next to her, but her father, always stubborn, took his bowl and spoon and sat down by the fire with his back to them.

Mike made a face at Ellen who frowned and shook her head at him warningly. Moira thought how hard it must be for her father to keep quiet. He loved to talk and when he was feeling good would sing Irish ballads or the London music hall numbers he had heard in Dublin. Usually he would pick up on one of Granda's grouchy remarks, despite Mama's warning and then a heated argument might start, but today he was keeping quiet and saving his energy for the performance tonight.

"Well I'm off," said Mike cheerfully, gulping the last of his tea. "So long everybody. Moira, be sure to give your mother a hand with the childer."

Ellen followed him to the door with Mickey tucked under her arm. Mike's bicycle stood in the front hall and he pulled it out and opened the door. He turned and kissed Ellen, whispering,

"God give me patience with him," and Ellen answered in a louder voice, "Thank God it's not raining yet. I hate to see you get drenched before you get to work."

She came back to the table and poured a mug of tea for her father, taking his empty bowl from him.

"Moira, are you finished? Go on up like a good girl and see if Eddie and Peggy are up, and help them get dressed," she said.

Moira could hear her little brother and sister upstairs, their bare feet pattering on the floor, as she climbed the stairs. It was Saturday, she thought gratefully, and there was no big hurry to get off to school.

Five year old Eddie, partially dressed, was looking for his shoes under the bed but Peggy, still in her flannel nightgown, had jumped back into bed and was hiding under the covers.

"If you don't get dressed and come downstairs, you won't get any breakfast. Mama's clearing the table right now," said Moira in the bossy tones she used to her younger brother and sister.

Peggy gave a smothered giggle under the covers and Eddie continued rummaging under the bed. They did not take Moira's threats seriously in the shelter of the home, though once away from the house, they took her hand obediently and looked up to her for protection against the dangers of the outdoors.

Moira pulled the blanket off Peggy and found her hugging Eddie's shoes. She tossed them to Eddie who muttered peevishly, "No wonder I couldn't find them."

When they were washed and dressed, she sent them down to the kitchen. Then, going over to her own bed, she pulled a book from under the pillow and settled down by the window, hoping for a little uninterrupted reading before her mother called her again.

The book was *Holidays among the Mountains,* and soon Moira was lost in the Welsh mountains with Beatrice, Sylvine and Jennie. As usual she lost track of time and was startled when she heard her mother's voice at the bedroom door.

"I thought I'd find you with your nose in a book," she said.

Moira sighed, put the book down reluctantly and began to help her mother make the beds. Mama sympathized with her love of reading and sometimes bought her penny fairytales when she went into Cavan town, but Mama never had time for reading and got impatient sometimes with so much work to do. Moira, as the eldest, had to help when she could.

"Someday you'll have a family of your own to take care of and you'll know what it is like, God help you," said her mother.

"I don't know," said Moira thoughtfully, "Maybe I'll be a nun. They must have plenty of time to read."

"Indeed they don't," said Mama. "When they're not on their knees praying, they're scrubbing and polishing. They have to wash clothes and cook meals just like everyone else."

That did not sound very promising to Moira. She thought about it.

"And another thing," said her mother. "They have to fast a lot. You wouldn't like that."

"Well, if I do get married, I'll just have two children, a boy and a girl, like the Protestants do," said Moira. She had always thought that was such a tidy arrangement, and wondered why Catholics had such large families, when they had so little money to take care of them. The Protestants she knew were well off by comparison.

Her mother laughed. "You'll take what God sends," she said. "Now be off with you and keep an eye on Eddie and Peggy. They're playing in front of the house and Mickey is asleep."

Mama had a way of ending the conversation just when it was getting interesting, and Moira felt she might get to know something about Protestants and Catholics and the mystery of large and small families.

Most of the day was spent out of doors except when an occasional shower drove them into the house. It was early April and the soft spring greens of the trees and bushes and the pale yellow primroses in the hedges filled Moira with a delight that made her run and jump with excitement, as the younger children followed her lead.

Her mother called them in about four o'clock and sent them upstairs to take a nap. Moira, who hadn't taken a nap in several years, protested, but when her mother warned her she would fall asleep at the play, she went obediently with the little ones.

Moira had planned to continue reading her book but her mother removed it and closed the curtains, so the room was in semi–darkness. Moira shut her eyes tightly and tried hard to fall asleep but it was no use. She tried reciting the multiplication table to herself and was up to six times seven, when she heard a knock on the front door downstairs. She pulled back the covers and tiptoed to the top of the stairs in time to hear her mother say,

"Paddy, what brings you here this time of day?"

"Is Mike home yet?" Moira recognized the voice of Paddy Doyle who played the part of Father Dolan in the play.

"I'm expecting him early, but he's not home yet. Is anything wrong?"

"Well I'm sure it's nothing that Mike can't fix. Two of the company have taken off for Dublin. There's rumors about an uprisin' and the two boyos are in with Sinn Fein, God help them," said Paddy.

"Poor Mike will be upset after all the work he put in on the play," said Mama, "Did they have big parts?"

"None at all. They were handlin' scenery and props. Sure they won't even be missed, but Mike may have to do a bit of scouting to get someone in their place. Well so long, ma'am. Tell Mike I'll see him at the hall."

Moira heard the door close and hurried off to bed. "Poor Dada," she thought. Why did they wait until the last minute? What was an uprisin'? There was a war on with Germany and there were many Irish fighting along with the British. She had heard her father say that when the war was over, England had promised Home Rule for Ireland. It was all very puzzling. She must remember to ask Dada about it.

When she heard her mother calling her, she realized she had fallen asleep after all. Eddie and Peggy were awake and running down the stairs.

"Come down and have some dinner. Your father's been home and taken off again to the hall. We'll follow along later," said her mother.

Moira wanted to ask about Paddy Doyle's visit, but remembered she was supposed to be in bed asleep at the time, and not listening at the top of the stairs. She had been called a Nosey Parker often enough.

"Where's Granda?" asked Moira when she came down to the kitchen and saw his armchair empty.

"He had his dinner and went off to visit one of his old cronies down the street," replied her mother.

"Is Granda going to the play too?" asked Eddie.

Moira knew better than to ask that question. Granda looked on play–acting as a lot of tommy–rot, and felt that his son–in–law's spare time would be better spent chopping wood for the fire or fetching water from the spring well instead of running off to re-hearsals when he came home from work.

"No, Granda will be home in bed sound asleep and so will you. Don't give Katie any trouble now," said Mama. Mama's friend Katie Dugan had been recruited to stay with the children, and would sleep over that night.

"He'll be no trouble," said Katie who had just arrived. "Sure they're grand childer."

Katie was short, plump, and rosy, in contrast to Mama who was tall and slim and had a lovely fair complexion. Mama looked very pretty tonight with her soft brown hair piled high on her head. Moira admired the new white blouse she was wearing, with lace at the throat and the tiny watch she had pinned to it that Dada had bought for her in Dublin.

"Drink up your milk, Moira. It's near time we were going," said her mother.

Moira gulped down her milk and ran upstairs to get her Sunday coat and hat. When she came down Mama was giving Katie last minute instructions about sending the children to bed not later than eight o'clock.

"You know how cranky me father gets when they're around him making too much noise."

"Don't worry," said Katie. "I'll be in bed early myself. I've had a hard day working for Madge. She's the divil to please."

Katie worked for a Mrs. Madge Malone who owned a grocery shop in the village and had living quarters above the shop. Katie did all the cleaning for both home and shop, did washing and ironing and cooking, but she was always very cheerful and ready to play with the children.

Mama kissed Eddie and Peggy. Mickey was already asleep in the cradle and Katie would carry him upstairs later and keep him in bed with her until they got home. There was a bottle of milk beside him in case he woke up, though Mama said it was a poor substitute for the real thing as she believed in nursing all her babies.

Moira and her mother got started at last, taking an umbrella with them although it looked clear, but you couldn't trust Irish weather and they might be coming home in a downpour.

When they got near the hall they would see people coming from all directions.

A play was a rare event in the parish. The young people had an occasional dance but there was little in the way of entertainment and traveling theatrical companies always bypassed the little village of Ballyhaise. Now they were having a play of their own with actors that most of them knew, and there was an air of excitement in the crowd. Her father had good seats for them down near the front and Moira sat down with her mother. People were greeting each other and stopping to talk to Mama but Moira sat staring at the curtain, not wanting to miss the first magic moment when it would go up and the play would begin. She could hear mysterious noises and whispering going on behind the curtain.

There were gas lamps on the walls around the hall. The only place she knew that had electric light was at the Department of Agriculture where Dada worked. Once when she had gone down to visit him there he had taken her into the dairy and told her to press the switch on the wall. The room was instantly filled with bright light like sunlight, leaving no dark corners, and she wished they could light like that at home instead of the lamps and candles that cast so many shadows.

The hall suddenly grew quieter and she saw that someone was going around turning out the gas lights, leaving only one or two flickering low. Then the curtain rose slowly.

The scene was the cottage of Arte O'Neil. There was a backdrop showing the ruins of a castle in the distance and beyond it the Atlantic Ocean. Moira thought it perfectly beautiful.

Claire Ffolliott was singing "Where are you going to my pretty maiden," while working at the milk churn in front of her cottage. Moira was lost in the enchantment of seeing it all come to life, having heard so many bits and pieces of it from her father. She was impatient when the curtain went down and the hustling and bustling went on as they changed the scenery around.

When Conn finally appeared wearing his old patched scarlet hunting coat and brown breeches with yellow top boots she could barely conceal her excitement.

"It's Dada," she whispered, squeezing her mother's arm. She must have said it too loudly as some of the audience looked in her direction, smiling and nodding.

Most of Conn's lines provoked gales of laughter and applause from the enthusiastic audience and Moira laughed too although she did not always understand the speeches. Her mother seemed to be enjoying herself, too, as though she had not heard the words many times before.

Sometimes there were long delays between the scenes and the audience would get very talkative. The noise behind the curtain was frantic and Moira wondered if her father had found someone to replace the two Sinn Feiners who had vanished so suddenly, or was he moving the scenery around all by himself.

Towards the end of the last act, her head felt heavy and she leaned against her mother's shoulder. She must have dozed off, for when her mother shook her, she opened her eyes suddenly to see all the cast standing in line on the stage bowing while everyone in the audience clapped loudly. She clapped too with the rest of them and the lights were turned up and people started to leave, talking and laughing as they went. Many of them stopped and leaned toward her mother, shaking her hand and saying things like, "Tell Mike he did a great job. We all had a grand time of it."

After the others had gone, they sat around waiting for her father. The curtain was up and presently he came out wiping the make-up off his face and called out, "Come on up here and see what it looks like from this angle."

Moira ran eagerly forward and climbed the steps to the stage. They had contrived makeshift dressing rooms with screens and the women were in one section and the men in another, and there was a great hurrying to and fro looking for belongings. The make-believe had vanished though everyone seemed happy and satisfied with the evening's work. As they came out dressed in their every day clothes, they spoke to Moira and her mother briefly and praised her father for his performance and for managing the production so well.

Presently her father came out again dressed in his own clothes and they started for home, Moira tired but still excited as she walked between her parents. It was an adventure just to be out so late, walking along the road at night. Sometimes she heard a rustle behind one of the dark hedges and wondered if some animal had been startled by the sound of their footsteps. She thought how frightened she would be if she had to come this way alone. She squeezed her father's hand tightly.

"Well Moira, how did you like the play?" he asked.

"It was all wonderful but you were the best of all," said Moira.

"Conn is a grand part, though I wouldn't mind playing Harvey Duff, the villain, sometime."

"Will the company start on another play soon?" asked Ellen.

"Not for a long time if at all. No more playacting for a while. I've got to start looking for a better job. With a growing family we can't manage on what I am making now."

"You mean Scotland, don't you?" said Ellen.

"Well there's no use going back to Dublin. Half the men there are out of work. There are plenty of jobs in Ayrshire at the Nobel factory."

"I can't leave my poor father all alone to go with you. It wouldn't be right. He's a sick old man. He'll take to his bed one of these days and there is no one but me to care for him."

Moira had heard this discussion before. She knew that her father planned to go alone to Scotland and when he had settled in a new job he would send for them. It was exciting to think of going to a new country and a new school, but she knew her mother worried a lot about being left alone with Granda and four small children.

They had arrived home and her father put the key in the lock and gave the door a push but it didn't open.

"God Almighty. He's bolted the door on the inside," he gasped.

"The old divil," said Ellen. "We'll have to go round the back way."

They groped their way around the house to the back yard, Mike leading the way. He put the key in the back door lock and gave a push but the door didn't budge.

"He's bolted this one too. The old bastard has locked us out."

"What'll we do? Shall I try to wake Katie by throwing something at the window?" said Ellen.

"Never mind. You might as well try to wake the dead. I know what I'll have to do."

He took off his shoe and quickly broke a pane of glass in the small window next to the door. They crept into the kitchen, wondering if they had awakened the old man, half expecting to hear him coming down the stairs, but all was quiet. Ellen groped her way to the table and lit the lamp. There was still some glow in the embers in the fireplace and she poked them and threw a few pieces of wood on the fire and it flared up cheerfully. She put the kettle on.

"I'm dying for a cup of tea," she said.

The Wake

Granda was dead. For many months he had lain in the big bed at the top of the stairs, a cranky invalid. Mama and I had run up and down those stairs a thousand times, bringing him soup, bread soaked in warm milk, and sometimes a cup of tea with a little whisky in it.

You were supposed to feel sad when someone in the family died, but the only sadness I could feel was for my mother, who burst into tears when the priest came and folded Granda's hands over his rosary and prayed and anointed him with the holy oils.

How could I feel sad for an old man who never said "Thanks!" no matter what I did for him, and once when I brought him his hot brick wrapped in flannel to warm his feet, he growled, "God Almighty child! Are you trying to burn me alive?"

Mama told me not to mind when I went downstairs and told her.

"He's not long for this world, poor soul. Try to be patient with him."

She put a slice of bread on the long toasting fork and gave it to me and I held it toward the red coals on the hearth fire.

"When he dies, will Dada come home from Scotland, and take us all to live there?" I asked.

"In God's good time. Don't be wishin' your grandfather's life away".

Now Granda was dead and a neighbor woman had come in and helped Mama wash him and lay him out in the brown burial habit, and the preparations for the wake were beginning. Mama was making Irish soda bread, and Mrs. Brady had brought a seed cake, and other neighbors were coming in and out with extra cups, glasses and chairs for the many friends and relatives who would come to pay their last respects.

I sat by the fire with my brother Eddie and sister Peggy and rocked the cradle where Baby Mickey slept. Sometimes a neighbor in passing would stop and pat one of us on the head, saying,

"Be good childer now. Your poor mother has her hands full this night."

Eddie and Peggy were getting heavy–headed with sleep and presently Mama took them off to bed, but she let me stay as I was wide awake, and besides I was seven years old and didn't always have to go to bed with the younger ones, though sometimes Eddie would protest and say, "Make Moira come too."

Tonight they were too sleepy to mind and I was relieved, and made myself busy putting more turf on the fire and prodding it with the poker.

I knew the younger ones hadn't given a thought to the problem that was bothering me. Our bedroom was on the far side of Granda's room and later I would lie up there, with the dead old man between me and the cheerful kitchen downstairs.

Tonight was the first night of the wake and only my mother and a few neighbors would sit by the fire, talking of old times and dozing in their chairs.

It would take until the next night to get the word around to my Granda's friends and the relatives in the outlying farms and then the house would be full of people. I settled down in the little chair beside the cradle, determined to stay awake all night.

Soon there was no one around but Mama and Katie, the neighbors having gone home to tend to their own families.

Katie lived far out in the country, but she had come to stay with us when my father went off to Scotland to work in the munitions plant where they made guns and bombs to fight the Germans.

In the daytime Katie worked for the McCallums who owned a grocery shop and a pub. When she came in to our place at night she put her foot up on a chair, pulled up her long black skirt and pulled a pint whisky bottle full of milk out of her stocking.

When we children drank a lot of milk during the day, sometimes there was not enough left over for the tea or cocoa we all had at bedtime and Katie's contribution was a godsend.

Once we had owned a cow but Granda had sold it, and I knew it was one of the things Mama could never quite forgive him for, because now we had to buy the milk at the grocery shop, where I took the quart can down every morning to be filled.

I asked Katie once if her bottle wasn't stolen since she hid it so carefully from her employer, and she was very indignant.

"They've got lashins and leavins of food in that house and the wee sup of milk I take would probably be given to the pigs."

The whisky bottle left a red shape on her plump leg but Katie said it would fade away in no time at all.

I drank the cup of cocoa Mama gave me and my eyelids began to feel heavy but when she said, "Why don't you go to bed?" I opened my eyes wide and sat up straight saying,

"I'm not a bit sleepy. Let me stay up a wee bit longer."

"She's afraid to be up there with the ould fella," said Katie.

"No I'm not." I glowered at her.

Mama said nothing but a little later when my head started to nod she said firmly, "Come on now. I'll take you up and tuck you in. You won't be going to school tomorrow but I'll need you up bright and early to run messages for me."

I knew it was no good to protest any further, so I followed her up the stairs and as we walked through Granda's bedroom, I kept my head turned away, but was conscious of the stillness and wished I could hear him grunting or snoring as usual. Mama waited, holding the candle while I got undressed and said my prayers. When I came to "God bless Granda" I stopped, puzzled.

"Say Lord have mercy on his soul," said Mama and I repeated the words adding for good measure "and on the souls of all the faithful departed," in case some of them might be hovering around.

"Can't you leave the candle for a little while?" She never liked to do this in case a sudden gust of wind from the window should tip it over and set fire to something but tonight she said,

"I'll leave it for now, but I'll come back when you are asleep and take it away."

I pulled the blanket over my head and began reciting, "Lord have mercy on his soul" to myself. I could hear the wind moaning in the trees outside and wondered if it was the banshee that mourns aloud when people die, or perhaps the souls in Purgatory who depend on our prayers to get them into Heaven. Now that I was alone in bed, I felt wide awake again and I could faintly hear the murmur of voices down in the kitchen. Sometimes the front door would open and I knew it was some neighbor dropping in to say,

"I'm sorry for your trouble, Mary Ellen. God rest his soul."

Eddie and Peggy slept soundly nearby and once Peggy gave a little cough in her sleep and turned over, and the sound cheered me up for a minute. Eddie always fell into a deep sleep as soon as his touched the pillow and I knew it would be very difficult to wake him up, and even if I did, Mama would be very annoyed with me.

I decided to say the rosary on my fingers, but the effort to keep count must have put me to sleep after all, because when I opened my eyes again, the daylight was showing through the curtains and I could hear Mama bustling around the kitchen, and Baby Mickey had begun to cry in his cradle by the fire.

I loved the early morning sounds and I got up and poured some water from the pitcher into the basin, washed my face and dressed quickly. Eddie and Peggy were still asleep, but I went over and shook Eddie by the shoulder. He mumbled "Le' me alone." and burrowed deep under the blankets. He was only five and when he awoke in the morning, he didn't always remember the things that had happened yesterday until I reminded him. I leaned over and whispered, "Wake up, Eddie. Granda died last night and we are going to have a wake and a funeral, and a lot of people will be coming."

He sat up startled, "And is Dada coming home, and are we going away in the big boat?"

"Not right away, silly. Mama has a lot of things to do first, like selling the land, and packing all our belongings, and first we have the funeral to take care of. I am going downstairs to help Mama. Do you want me to help you get dressed?"

"I can dress myself," he said, pushing away. I had helped him until he was five, but I left him alone now, though I knew he still might put his jersey on backward or inside out.

Peggy still slept, but she was only three, and would not understand all the exciting things that were happening.

Now I walked through the other bedroom and with all my daytime bravery, I glanced over at Granda. He looked very peaceful and I did not feel afraid of him any more.

Mama had a pot of stirabout with tea and toast for breakfast and when I came downstairs, she filled a bowl with the steaming porridge and poured milk over it.

"Eat up now. I want you to go to Farrelly's and get me some groceries. We'll need extras for the next couple of days with all the people coming."

"How will they know about Granda? Don't his relatives live in Castletara?" I asked.

"I got Maggie Riordan to send a wire to your father last night and before the day is over, the whole county will have the word."

Maggie Riordan ran the post office and the telegraph office in our village and was a good source of information about all the social happenings.

I finished my breakfast and took the list Mama had made.

"Tell him to put it in the book, and I'll be down to pay him later—and walk quietly down the road—no buck–jumping. We are a house of mourning."

"I'll walk like Della Smith," I said. Della Smith was one of my school chums whose father owned the mill outside the village. She always wore pretty clothes and walked like a prim little lady, while I was given to running and leaping like a foal in a field.

All that day I was kept busy, either going on errands or minding the baby and toward evening Mama had us put on our best clothes to look nice for the company. I had a white starched pinafore over my navy wool dress.

The whisky and glasses were on the table in the corner of the kitchen and the large table was set with cakes and soda bread and some cold meats. The big brown teapot waited there to be filled, and the yellow tea cosy that we put over the pot to keep it hot.

I enjoyed listening to the conversations which seemed to follow a pattern. First it was the customary,

"I'm sorry for your trouble ma'am. Poor ould Ned. He was a good man, Lord rest his soul."

They all said that at a wake, even if they didn't believe it because it was a bad thing to speak ill of the dead. The old people always wanted details about the last minutes of the departed, and I wondered if my mother didn't get awfully tired of repeating them.

"I brought him up a soft boiled egg and a piece of toast, and propped him up with the pillows, but he barely touched a thing. One of the last things he said to me was, 'Keep the land for Edward.'"

"Ah sure, he was fond of his little grandson," one of the farmers broke in, "He would want him to be a farmer like himself."

Being a farmer, and owning a piece of land and a few cows and chickens was the main ambition of most of the men, except for the more adventurous ones like my father, whose heart was set on going to America where four of his older brothers had gone years before.

I couldn't see my brother Eddie as a farmer either. Even though he was only five, what he liked best were trains and motor cars. We didn't see many cars in Ballyhaise, but every once in a while the Protestant bishop drove through the village and Eddie would run to the front door shouting, "a motor car!, a motor car!" and his eyes would shine with delight.

My mother continued her story. "I could see he was sinking fast and I sent Moira to fetch Mrs. Brady, and to ask Pat Brady to go for the priest, but by the time Father Kelly got here my father was gone. Thank God, he had made his confession and received Holy Communion only the day before."

The old people shook their heads and murmured in sympathy then went upstairs to kneel by the bed and say a few prayers for the departed. When they came down the men headed for the table where the whisky stood. They called it "a wee drop of courage", and after a few more references of Granda, they switched to talk of crops and cattle, the war in Europe and the Sinn Feiners. I tried to listen but didn't understand most of it.

"Did you hear that Mike Fagan has joined the Sinn Feiners?" whispered one.

"That corner-boy!" said another angrily. "God help Ireland if she's depending on him. He'd be better off if he joined up and fought the Germans. It would make a man of him."

"You want him to go out and help the bloody English? Let them fight their own wars and be damned to them."

When the arguments got louder one of the women would say, "Hould your whisht. Have you no respect for the departed upstairs?" and the men would quiet down for a while.

As she had done the night before, Mama took the younger children up to bed. She had carried the cradle up to the bedroom during the day and Baby Micky was asleep upstairs.

I helped pass around tea and cake to the women and sat down next to Cousin Benny who though a grown man was always friendly and good natured with children.

"I didn't know Granda had so many friends and relatives," I whispered to him.

"Well now," said Benny, "an Irish wake is a social affair and even if they didn't know your Granda, they'd come anyway to meet old friends, to say nothing of having a wee drop of the crathur, to help them forget their troubles."

"My father can't get home for the funeral because of his job. Mama got a wire from him, but he is coming next month to take us to Scotland," I told him.

"Won't you be sorry to leave Ireland, Moira?"

"Well, I'm looking forward to travelling in the train and ship and see new places, and we can always come back to visit."

"They never come back, once they go, Moira," he said sadly, "Ireland is a poor country."

"I'll come back, Benny," I promised.

The fire glowed warm and I felt cosy and safe, listening to the murmur of voices. I did not remember falling asleep but Mama was shaking me, and telling me to come to bed, and I was too tired to protest.

Later in bed I was awakened by the drone of voices from the bedroom next door and I knew that the priest was there, leading the mourners in the recital of the sorrowful mysteries of the rosary. I wondered if Father Kelly would want "a wee drop of the courage" or if his own brand of spiritual courage was enough for him.

There was another day and night of the wake but finally the morning of the funeral came and we dressed in our Sunday best with our warmest coats for the long trip to the cemetery. Baby Mickey and Peggy were left in the care of one of the neighbors while Eddie and I went to the funeral mass with Mama.

As we walked up the chapel road we overtook other villagers, the women with shawls wrapped around their heads against the chill morning air. They nodded to us with serious faces and muttered words of consolation to my mother, but I missed the cheerful "Top o' the mornin'" which I usually heard going to early mass.

It was cloudy with a threat of rain and I hoped the sun would come out by the time we left mass to go to the graveyard.

Granda's coffin stood on a pedestal just outside the altar rails with six tall candles around it, and as we came into the church, one of the altar boys came out and lit the candles. We followed Mama to the altar rail to kneel and say a prayer but all that would come to mind was the rhyme,

> "My coffin shall be black
> Six angels at my back,
> Two to sing and two to pray
> And two to carry my soul away."

Then we went back and took our seats, and the priest, wearing his black outer vestments came out and started the requiem mass.

I tried to feel properly sad and reverent but my mind kept wandering. A few months before, I had made my first communion here with my class from school, and then everything had been white and cheerful. I had a new white dress and veil for the occasion and the boys had worn navy blue suits, and we all behaved as though we were very holy and incapable of mischief.

I had often heard the saying "The happiest day of your life is the day of your first communion," and I kept waiting for that miraculous moment when that wonderful glow of happiness would descend on me and fill me with the ecstasy that the saints and martyrs had felt. I closed my eyes and concentrated very hard, but all I could think of was how hungry I was, as it was the first time I had fasted from midnight and come to mass without any breakfast. I knew what the feeling should be like but I had only felt it when I was running wildly through the fields, or walking in the woods when the spring flowers were blooming.

When I explained this to Mama later she said I sounded more like a pagan than a Christian and that I should make an act of contrition to make sure I was in a state of grace.

Kneeling up straight was very tiring and I leaned back against the seat. My brother Eddie was sitting down but of course he was not a real Catholic yet, as he would not make his First Communion for two more years.

The old stone chapel was divided into three sections, all facing the main altar, and over one section was a small gallery where the same people sat Sunday after Sunday. One gallery was called the Burke gallery because Schoolmaster Burke and his wife and family always sat there. With my forehead pressed against the wooden seat in front of me, I could imagine all the faces in their proper places and would have been surprised to look up and find that someone had chosen a different seat.

A nudge from my mother made me suddenly aware that we had come to the end of the funeral service, and with a feeling of guilt for my lack of attention, I whispered a few rapid prayers for my dead grandfather.

Six of the men carried the coffin outside and placed it in the hearse, drawn by two black horses which waited in the chapel yard.

My mother was taking Eddie in a pony and trap which had been loaned for the occasion and a couple of the old women relatives of my Granda joined her.

I was to ride in a side car or jaunting car as we called it when it was used for more lively occasions. It was less comfortable than the trap, but more exciting to ride on with its high seats back to back. Cousin Benny sat beside me, and I knew Mama had warned him not to let me fall off when we travelled over the rutted muddy lanes.

It took about an hour to ride out to the cemetery, and when we passed the fields where men were working, they would stop and remove their caps and make the sign of the cross out of respect.

I had set my face in a serious expression for the solemn occasion, but I was really enjoying the rare treat of a ride through the country lanes, now that the early morning clouds had passed and the sun was shining.

At last we came to the cemetery and we went through the iron gates, past old and new graves, many of the tombstones so overgrown with weeds and grass that you could not read the names.

We stopped at the newly dug grave with mounds of earth all around it. The mourners stood in a semi–circle, while the priest said the burial service. He said it in Latin mostly but I recognized the part about "ashes to ashes, and dust to dust" which I thought very solemn and poetic. Then he sprinkled holy water on the coffin and it was lowered into the ground.

Mama stood for a few minutes praying, then taking Eddie and me by the hand she turned away and took us back to the waiting trap.

This time I rode with Mama and Eddie and Cousin Benny in the trap, the old people having arranged to go home in another direction. Mama and Benny talked about Granda and things that happened long before I was born, but soon I stopped listening.

I wanted to think about what was coming next: our leaving Ireland for a new life in Scotland, and after the war was over, if Father had his way, we would go to America, where there were no banshees nor leprechauns and where the Souls in Purgatory did not moan in the trees late at night.

A War Time Voyage

Where was the sea? She had looked forward so much to seeing the sea for the first time. It would be blue–green with white capped waves, flowing on to golden sand. There would be sea shells and star fish scattered here and there and children would be making castles with brightly coloured pails and shovels, like the pictures in "A Child's Garden of Verses".

Living in an inland Irish county Mother had often told her how beautiful the sea was in Dublin at Sandycove with seagulls swooping and dipping to touch the waves. Moira had been two years old when they had left Dublin to return to her Grand-father's farm in northern Ireland and she could not recall anything about Dublin or the sea.

Now they were going to Scotland in a ship and somewhere out there was the sea, but it was very different from the one in her imagination. The black choppy water where boats creaked and groaned in the shadows, as if reluctant to leave the dock was frightening, but had a different kind of beauty. She stared out through the fog and rain knowing she would remember this sight for a long time.

The Belfast streets were wet and dismal in the lamplight. Moira with her mother, father and three younger children were one of the little groups of bedraggled travellers, carrying suitcases and bundles, struggling along the dock to the small ship that would take them to Scotland.

She could hear a variety of Irish brogues, mingled with Scottish burrs and clipped English accents. Her eight year old mind was dizzy with the impressions she was absorbing. She watched the mothers, their heads darting from side to side anxiously as they herded their children together; the fathers plodding ahead with the heaviest luggage calling back warnings and assurances.

Her father worked for the Nobel Company in Scotland. Somewhere among the sand dunes and the heather there was a little town where the weapons of war were manufactured and where they would live. After a lonesome year in a boarding house

Father had come back to Ireland to bring the family to make a new home in war–time Britain.

Now he plodded ahead of them on the gloomy Belfast dock, his large Gladstone bag clutched in his right hand, while he carried Baby Mickey on his left arm. Moira walked behind with her six year old brother Eddie by the hand while her mother followed close with four year old Peggy.

"Mike, for the love of God, will you slow up. The children can't keep up with you." Mama called out.

But Mike had already stopped and put his bag down.

"They're turning people away at the boat." he said. "In God's name, what's going on?"

He grabbed at a man heading back along the dock muttering to himself.

"What's the matter?" he inquired anxiously.

"They say there's German mines in the channel. The bloody Huns will blow the boat up," came the angry reply.

A less excitable gentleman seeing their distress said kindly, "They say there will be a delay of about an hour. We are to wait in the shed until they let us know."

They followed him back some distance with the others. The shed was a large barn–like waiting room with wooden benches where families were settling down for a dreary wait, consoling the children with biscuits and chocolate bars.

Mike found a vacant seat for Mama and put Baby Micky on her lap. He pulled the other children around her.

"Stay close to Mama! Sit on the luggage! I'll see what I can find out, Ellen. It shouldn't be too long"

"Mike," whispered Mama anxiously, "Do you think it's safe? Maybe we should go back home and wait until the war's over."

"Now, now! These boats run three or four times a day and nothing has happened yet. It's probably just a rumor," Mike said.

"How about the *Lusitania*?" said Mama.

That was in the Atlantic Ocean. This is the North Channel. "It's just a few hours trip to Scotland," Mike said confidently.

"But Dada," interrupted Moira, "On the map you showed me, the North Channel flows into the Atlantic Ocean."

"Be quiet, Moira. The British Navy would never let them get this close."

That is true, Moira thought. Even the Irish admitted that Britannia ruled the waves. Mostly they said it scornfully and there were even some Irishmen who wanted the Germans to win the war. Politics were very confusing. To Catholics like herself the English Protestant settler was the enemy but the one person she would miss most in Ballyhaise was Mrs. Clintwell or "Mama Clinta" as they had called her.

"Mama Clinta" was a Protestant and an Orangewoman, but she had enriched Moira's life with a collection of children's books that had belonged to her now grown–up daughter. Schoolmaster Burke had books but he kept them under lock and key and it would have been unthinkable to ask for the loan of one.

Moira looked around the shed and watched as strangers began talking to each other as if each hoped that others would have the solution to their problems. Here and there bottles were pulled out and passed around.

Mama had found a friend in a pleasant–faced woman who sat next to her and who had a plump baby in her lap and a three year old standing close to her. Both little girls had a mop of natural curls, a feature Moira noticed at once and envied. She would be happy to exchange her straight black hair for brown gold ringlets.

"This is my oldest, Moira," said her mother, pulling her forward. "Moira, this is Mrs. Whyte. Her husband works for Nobel too."

"Hello, Moira," said Mrs. Whyte with a friendly smile. "This is Meg and the baby is Gretta."

The two mothers were glad to have found each other and continued talking, though Mama darted frequent anxious glances toward the door where Father had vanished earlier.

Presently he came hurrying back, wearing that look of cheerful optimism which usually concealed his anxiety. He announced, "They expect to sail about nine o'clock. That gives us a two hour wait. There's a tea room a few doors down where you can have a cup of tea and something to eat. It'll kill the time and make you feel a lot better."

"Are you sure, Mike, that we have enough time? Maybe we had better stay where they can find us."

"They'll find us. I talked to one of the officers and he said someone would round up everyone when they were ready to sail."

Many of the passengers had drifted out of the shed mostly to find the nearest pub and the tired little family followed Mike out again into the rain–swept streets.

Mama had introduced Mrs. Whyte to Father and he had suggested that she join them, but she had decided to stay in the shed where she and the little girls would be warm.

"If they eat again they might get seasick!" she explained.

Moira had never been seasick and she couldn't imagine the sensation. She felt hungry after the long train ride from home to Belfast, and the chilly weather had given them all an appetite.

The tea room was pleasantly cheerful in contrast to the gloom outside and they found an empty table. One overworked waitress was hurrying about, trying to keep up with orders from this unexpected flow of customers.

"We can give you a plate of buttered bread and some buns with your tea, but that's all we have," she said when Father finally got her attention.

She brought a large brown pot of tea to the table, and Mama poured. She always gave the children cocoa at home but Mrs. Whyte's comment about seasickness made her decide that tea might be a safer beverage. They began to feel more cheerful as they began to sip the steaming liquid.

"Eat some bread and butter first. Then you can have a bun," said their father as he passed the plates around.

Mama gave a deep sigh of satisfaction.

"Nothing like a good cup of tea," she said. Moira had heard her say this many times. Tea gave her the same glow of well–being that many men got from whisky, and she was now prepared to face the dangers of the voyage. Baby Micky now slept on her lap, oblivious to all the excitement and Peggy was beginning to nod at the table.

The door of the tea room swung open suddenly and a booming voice called, "Any passengers for the Ardrossan boat? We'll be on our way.

The scene became one of bustle and confusion as the children and luggage were rounded up, and the waitress dashed around, making sure that all bills were paid.

This time they reached the end of the dock, hurrying through the rain and a gusty wind that made umbrellas useless. Two seamen stood at the gangplank steadying the passengers as they struggled on board. Moira caught a glimpse of the black water beneath her and the boat seemed to be rocking unpleasantly. Her father hurried them to a large salon where the other passengers had assembled. Mrs. Whyte was already there and Mama found seats near her and settled down to continue this new friendship. There was a porthole above their seats and Eddie stood up and tried to peer out but there was only fog and rain to be seen and he sat down.

Mama pulled on Father's arm and whispered something in his ear. He nodded and turning, took Eddie by the hand.

"Come with me, son," he said.

"Where are you going?" demanded Moira, not wanting to be left out of any new adventure.

"To see a man about a dog," answered Father as he marched Eddie off.

Moira sat down, knowing this meant they were going to look for a mens' W.C. She knew that when he came back he would have directions for the women's room also. Mama would have seen to that. She listened as her mother and Mrs. Whyte began exchanging family history.

Mrs. Whyte had lived in Scotland for some time and had been home to Ireland to visit her invalid mother. She expected her husband to meet her in Ardrossan when the boat arrived, but with this unforseen delay, she did not know what to expect and how she would get to her town which was more than a mile away.

"We are supposed to catch the train that meets the boat and travels up to Glasgow. We call it the boat train and it stops at all the little towns on the way, but now we may miss it."

"We have to catch that boat train too," said Mama. "We're on our way to Stevenston."

"That's the next town to ours. Well, we'll all be together. Just pray the Lord is watching over us this night."

Mama sighed. "I always swore I'd never set foot on a ship of any kind, and if God spares me to get off this one, Mike will never get me to go on the water again."

"Ah now, it's not always this bad. You'll want to visit Ireland again when the war is over and you can travel in the summer. It can be a nice trip in the daytime when the sun is shining and you can sit up on deck." Mrs. Whyte said consolingly.

"I'll have no reason to go back. My mother and father are both gone now, Lord have mercy on them. Mike can go home by himself if he wants to," replied Mama.

A loud horn from somewhere above interrupted them, and Father and Eddie came hurrying back at that moment.

"We're on our way. They say there is no danger from the mines, but we are in for a stormy crossing," he announced.

There was a churning sound as the boat pushed its way out into the Channel. Some of the older Irish women clutched rosaries in their fingers, but Mama and Mrs. Whyte and the other mothers in the salon busied themselves making their children comfortable and watching for the first signs of sea sickness.

Exhaustion had triumphed over sea sickness with most of the children, though their parents would stay awake throughout the voyage.

Moira closed her eyes but this made her more conscious of the heave and swell of the boat and she sat up suddenly, holding her stomach. Her father grabbed her by the arm and rushed her out on deck. He held her as she leaned over the rail.

Presently she began to feel better. The wet wind revived her but she shivered in the cold. People on deck were clinging to each other as the boat heaved from side to side.

"You'll be able to sleep now," said her father. "You are over the worst of it. Now, let's get inside before we get washed overboard."

They hurried in to the warm salon and soon she was curled up on the hard bench beside her brother. The sound of the wind and the waves soon became part of her dreams as the ship ploughed through the storm, carrying them toward a new life.

Maxine Zalkin
Blue Eyes

She had blue eyes, cold icy cold sparkling blue eyes. Not baby blue. She used them, wide eyed, to hype those around her although you would never guess she was doing it because her personality was so spanking sparkling and her eyes looked at you sparkling and innocent and she really was innocent. She really didn't know, at least not consciously, she really didn't see what it was that she was doing, what it was that she wanted from people besides attention. She just wanted attention. That was innocent enough, wasn't it? Only attention didn't end there. She wanted more and then more and more and then she wanted yours. All of yours. All of the attention that someone might have been willing to give to you she took, and she wasn't satisfied with that. She wanted all of everybody's attention. All of it. She didn't want them to stop giving her attention for a minute so they could get their income tax done or something. If they stopped for a minute to get their income tax done she went on to someone else and made them pay for it by passing them by next time. No next times. No chance to make up for it. Too late. She had wanted it when she wanted it and if you didn't give it she went on to someone else. She didn't know she had a disease and that she would need a psychiatrist and that she would need all of the psychiatrist's hours not just one a week or two a week sixty minute hours that ended. No. She would need more. She would need all of his hours and all of him. She would devour him too. She would devour the psychiatrist and go on to other psychiatrists until there were no more psychiatrists left, and then she would go on to encounter groups and gurus. And when there was no more family or friend or psychiatrist or encounter group or guru left she would devour herself. She knew it. She had known it somewhere deep down inside her which was what made her sparkling blue eyed personality seem so frantic instead of so cute and sweet.

Maxine Zalkin

Unconsenting Adult

I am sexed to death
and I am bored
by tests
one in every magazine
that tell me how good a lover I am
or am not
how inhibited
and how the authors of these tests
now free me
for everything
and anything is o k
whatsoever

first of all
I want some limits
but I don't want them to set them
I don't want
for example
I don't want sperm shooting into my mouth
what would I do with it
swallow it
someone told me once if I swallow watermelon seeds
I would grow a watermelon in my stomach
would I spit it out
where
how Emily Post
maybe I have not got over my need
for titties or bottle nipples
the edges of ragged blankets
or crawling on the floor putting small pieces of lint into
my mouth

if I now smoke a cigarette a Mammy Yokum pipe or a thin
black cigar
the surgeon general gets into the act
my private consenting act
and tells me with the voice of absolute authority
it is dangerous to my health as if his objectivity
could be my reason
but I don't need the surgeon general
to tell me
I don't need any more objective authorities
to cheapen my private consenting acts by
insinuating themselves into my own
philosophical question
what is health

If I know it isn't
they are there saying
if it doesn't feel right for you
you aren't ready for it
yet
but there they are
with their anything goes
as if they have to tell me
as if they have to say it
or I won't know

I don't want to be told
what is right
I don't like their sitting there in
their talk show chairs
telling me

with their absolute authoritarian expertise
that anything goes
I want privacy
in the privacy of my own home
between consenting adults
to find out for myself
what feels right for me
without their telling me I must find out for my self
I don't want their smeary words making smudges
on the insides of my private spaces
their kind of ubiquitous graffiti
the smug look of their objective approach
their busy bodies flying around the country
appearing here and there
in New York and San Francisco
and on everyone's car radio and
television screen
insinuating themselves into rights
they don't have and I don't give them
but they take anyway
to be all pervasive
to tell me
and my children
what's normal
in the privacy of my
own home
in the privacy
of my bedroom
under my covers
between two consenting child adults

Mary Tolman Kent
The Yellow Jaguar

ometimes, still, Patricia winces, remembering the fine old vintage car. By now the canary yellow must have faded to a lusterless nothing. Full of dents, bumpers hanging and doors held shut with clothesline, it has probably joined some rural dump and sags in briars or rusted coils of wire.

Sometimes she cries, as she almost did all those years ago on their way to visit Allen's daughter, Dawn. Six hundred long miles north of L.A. they'd turned off Highway 101 and headed west when suddenly they burst from the redwood forest into a landscape so battered by long ago loggers and subsequent erosion that even Allen, the unflappable newspaperman, exploded.

"Goddamned lumber barons, leaving their shit around."

His thigh beneath her hand tensed, his jaw jutted forward, and even from his profile she knew that his eyes and mouth slashed the look of contempt across his heavy face. Recklessly he drove into the afternoon sun, twisting along the country road that curved with the river. She stared at the tree trunks spilled like giant matchsticks down the raw red earth, clotting the river below. It was a battlefield.

"Watch for the store," he said, slowing the yellow Jaguar as they passed a scattering of shanties. "Dawn said the turn-off is a quarter mile beyond the store."

At the mention of Dawn, Patricia's hands began to sweat, the pulse in her throat to throb, pressing up her neck and into her ears. Dawn was Allen's daughter, but all the children—two his, three hers—seemed to have become "theirs" somewhere along the fifteen years of marriage, and Patricia was afraid for Dawn. Or *of* her, perhaps?

"Granville Country Store," a rainbow of orange and blue arched above the veranda of a weather-beaten shed. In pantomime a ragged group stared from blank faces at the yellow

Jaguar cruising by. But that wasn't Dawn, thank God, with the baby on her hip, nor that other girl with bare feet poking out below her trailing skirt. Their clothes were so muted with time and filth that Patricia felt ill. She pressed her hands against her nose, knowing the powerful stench as though it were trapped in the car with her. They cruised on by, safe this time. Still, Patricia crossed her fingers, sat stiffly in the beige bucket seat as though in a dentist's chair, braced for unknown shocks to her system. If only Dawn didn't have that vacant look in her eyes, Patricia thought she might stand anything.

A quarter of a mile beyond the Granville Country Store they turned off the road and onto a dirt track, past a tumble–down house apparently held together with the wisteria that twined around the rails and posts of the porch and spread across the roof in a riot of purple. Patricia's knotted muscles began to relax. This house was quaint, as long as it wasn't Dawn's but belonged to that bare–breasted woman who smiled from the vegetable patch, a toddler by her side.

"A pretty little place," Patricia blurted out in a foolish frenzy of relief.

"Pretty! Jesus! For chrissake, Trish, that's the kind of poverty I came from. Remember? So don't give me your dreamy, squint–eyed interpretations on the beauty of the simple life. Oh my God," he said, his voice wailing with disgust, "I can just imagine how you'd paint that scene—the underfed wench back there, an ethereal saint; and the grubby kid, a wide–eyed gamin from the romantic streets of Paris. I bet she's got VD!"

He, too, was scared to death, Patricia realized, with a wave of tenderness for this self–made man. She looked through the dusty window, seeking out some beauty to sustain her hope and melt away the icy stone that grew in her gut. And at last the country she'd imagined from Dawn's letters began to emerge. Brushed by the limbs of overhanging trees, the car wound slowly upward through madrones and oaks, across the meadow strewn with pale blue iris, and there, marking the place, stood Dawn's old VW bus.

"Sorry, Trish," he said, and parked behind the bus.

"That's okay," she said.

He carried the styrofoam ice box, she carried a jug of red wine, and they started up the steep path.

"Hello, you beautiful people," Dawn called, and a sob of relief rose in Patricia's throat at the sight of the sun–bleached hair streaming every which–way as Dawn ran toward them down the hill.

"Honey–Bear," Allen said huskily into Dawn's plump neck as he lifted her off her feet.

"Dawn, it *is* lovely here after all," Patricia said.

"After all? After all what, Trish?"

"Oh, I don't know. The long trip, I guess," Patricia said, blushing.

"Yeah, well, anyway, you're here, and in time to see the sunset too! You can help Barnie bring in the goats, Daddy. But come on, let me carry something. Where's your suitcase?"

"We're staying at a motel back on the highway," Allen said.

"That's a lousy redneck joint," Dawn said.

Now Patricia understood that motel woman's glance as they registered and asked the way to Granville. Standing there behind the counter with her hair in curlers, her huge arms akimbo, she'd said, "Your daughter a hippy?"

And now Dawn gave Patricia a withering look that blamed the stepmother for everything. She grabbed the jug of wine, but finally shrugged, then smiled. "Thanks, Trish, I knew you'd bring some goodies."

They trudged up the path, Patricia and Allen soon winded and speechless. At last the cabin came into sight, perched on a knoll, an alpine setting with conifers towering over this timid imprint on the land. As they got closer, though, signs of human endeavor assailed them—chickens, ducks, turkeys running and squawking all over the place; a garden fenced from animal marauders with scraps of wood and wire; a bathtub sitting in the middle of nowhere; and finally Barnie coming toward them with the baby in his arms.

"Whew, quite a climb," Allen said, stopping to catch his breath. "Hey there, little fella, are you my grandson?" he called out, and they walked on toward the tall lean man that Dawn lived with now.

Not at all like Kenneth, Patricia thought, comparing Barnie to Dawn's ex–husband. She desperately wanted to like this man, for he was the baby's father. No doubt about it—identical dimpled grins and dark complexions. The baby's mop of chestnut curls, his eyes like wet black pebbles confirmed the fact. Now he chortled at Allen, and when Barnie passed him to his grandfather, Patricia restrained her reaching arms.

Later, when the men went off to get the goats, she lay on the grass with the baby on her tummy, and eyeball to eyeball they became acquainted. No matter that at eight months old he had no name. He would choose his own, Dawn said. He stuck his finger in Patricia's eye and crowed at his discovery.

"Oh baby darling," she murmured, hugging him so tight that he cried.

She handed him to Dawn and watched him nurse, his mouth and fingers pressed into Dawn's breast while his toes wiggled in rhythmic accompaniment to his ecstasy. Perhaps the baby and all this loveliness justified everything, she thought, gazing into the valley and across to the mountains beyond.

The bathtub, sitting in the prime view spot, its claw feet firmly implanted in the wildflowers, was a slapstick defiance of one culture by another. She tried to visualize the family scene— chubby pink Dawn, skinny dark Barnie, and the baby sitting naked in the tub enjoying the view. And where were all of Dawn's fluffy trousseau towels now? she wondered, remembering Dawn and Kenneth vowing everlasting love beside the swimming pool. Well, nothing was everlasting; even now the hills turned lavender before Patricia's eyes.

"How nice," she said, hugging her knees.

"Yes," Dawn said.

"You're getting on all right?"

"Oh sure. And wait til you see everything; you'll like it, I think... Trish, how's Daddy? He really looks wiped out."

"Well, yes. Of course. He's been worried about you, among other things."

"God, why me? I'm fine. Can't he see that?"

"Oh Dawn."

"Well, can't he?" Dawn persisted.

"He will. Just give him time. I'm sure that the reality of that precious baby will help a lot...

Oh, the kids all send their love." And what could they talk about now? Patricia discarded one dangerous topic after another.

"How are they?" Dawn helped her out. "Is Joanie still into creative dance?"

"Oh no, it's archeology now. And Ben thinks he'll be a potter. Did I write you that? Angel's in love with an entire rock band..."

Dawn laughed. "And Joe? Still Mr. Straight?"

"I hate that word, but yes, I guess he is. Very responsible, you know, carrying everyone's worries around with him. He doesn't have any fun."

"Are people supposed to have fun?"

"I saw Kenneth at the museum the other day. He asked about you. He's married again, you know."

"Now there's a guy who likes his fun...Well, come on, baby. I'll put you in the cradle and start supper. Just sit, Trish. I'll bring you some wine."

Sipping from a jelly glass, Patricia sat on a rock, trying not to hear the jumble in her head, listening instead to the soothing silence, and then to the bells of six goats that tinkled around the brow of the hill. The men followed, and against the purple sky they were two flat cartoons: Allen—bulky, square–jawed, hands stuffed in his pockets; Barnie—a stick figure, hands gesticulating.

"I don't suppose you serve cocktails around here, but I sure could use a snort of something," Allen said as he slumped down on the doorstep. Dawn brought him some wine, and he and Patricia watched Barnie milk the goats for awhile, then went inside.

"I'm sorry, I'm not much good with a wood stove, Dawn, but we brought some steaks," Patricia said.

She looked around the room. A sleeping loft covered about a quarter of the ceiling space. Over the stove and sink pots hung on the wall. A kerosene lamp cast a pool of light on the round table. And off in a shadowy corner stood a cradle. Stuck in milk cartons, burned out pots, plants grew everywhere.

"Where's the john?" she asked.

"Anywhere down hill from the spring," Dawn said as she chopped up carrots and peppers for salad. "The shovel and toilet paper are on the porch."

Patricia groped her way through the dusk toward a clump of trees, scattering a bunch of chickens who squawked around her feet. She squatted in the bushes, not sure whether to laugh or cry.

"But goddamnit, Dawn, food stamps aren't meant for people like you!" Allen glared at his plate, then stabbed a piece of steak with his fork and jammed it into his mouth.

"Why not? What do you mean? Just what am I like, Daddy? Come on, what do you mean?"

"Jesus, honey, you're educated!"

"Oh shit, EDUCATED! That's the biggest rip–off of all. I had to *de*–educate myself to even do what I want to do."

"Well, what in hell do you want to do?" Allen asked, his face growing dangerously red.

The baby screamed and Barnie brought him to Dawn. She grabbed him and shoved his teary face up under her T–shirt to nurse.

"Teach kids! I've started a school!" she said.

"Oh ho! I thought you didn't approve of education," Allen said.

"Dessert anyone?" Patricia asked, peeling an orange.

"It's a free school," Barnie said, reaching for an orange segment, "that's different."

"You know, these kids have weird backgrounds," Dawn said, her face softening as she explained about the broken homes, the hippies and ex–hippies, the addicts and ex–addicts, the homosexuals and bi–sexuals that were these children's parents. "A lot of them are just generally spaced. Their kids don't fit into the town school because their hair's too long, or they won't wear shoes, or they just can't deal with rules. Oh, they know all about sex, dope, how to kill a chicken, stuff like that. But it's a real challenge to teach them to read."

Dawn put the baby back in the cradle and they took their wine glasses out to the grassy slope.

"Got any doctors around here, hospitals?" Allen asked.

"Why? Are you sick, Daddy?"

"No, no. I'm just a little concerned about sanitation, you know, medicine, shots. Is the baby getting his shots?"

"There's some so–so doctors in town, a rinky–dink hospital." Barnie said.

"The baby's fine. Don't worry, Daddy, he's had his shots."

"Last year there was a little dysentery going around," Barnie said, "Some clap, one O.D., but generally folks around here eat right and live without hassles, so they're pretty healthy."

Covering her ears, Patricia lay flat on her back and looked for the Milky Way. Infinite space, once a terrifying concept, now hypnotized her as she gazed into a billion stars.

Enclosed in the car with the familiar smell of worn leather and Allen's Camel cigarette, Patricia almost fell asleep. But a jumble of jargon swirled graffiti words around and around in her head, giving her vertigo. And Allen was grumping.

"Barnie makes my belly ache. Give me a Rolaid...please," he said.

"The baby's lovely, isn't he?" she said, rummaging in the glove compartment among the familiar props—kleenex, flashlight, maps, aspirin, whiskey, cigarettes and Rolaids. She handed him a pill.

At last across the night fluorescent tubes of light scrawled "Sleepytime Haven," and inside with the motel furnishings that one encounters from one end of the U.S.A. to the other, Patricia felt at home, both deprecating and adoring the luxurious bad taste.

Turquoise blue and burnt sienna roses splashed across the mammoth bed. Huge lamps failed to cast their 150 watt light anywhere near where it would be needed should she wish to read those back issues of *The New Yorker* she'd brought along, though they seemed quite irrelevant now. Motel rooms were not for reading, but for watching TV, stretched out, sipping scotch. And this room provided a vibrating mattress, that quaint pre–waterbed fad.

"Five minutes for a quarter," she said.

"Just what we need for relaxation after all that peace and tranquility," he said as they lay on the bed with their shoes off, gently jiggling and watching the eleven o'clock news across the bulk of his Madras shirt.

The news, whatever it was, as usual inspired their derision of the system, the politicians, the media, though individual newsmen were, of course, judged on their merits. So how come they came down so hard on Dawn for going a few steps further in the same direction? The everlasting generational problem, she supposed, as she accidentally knocked over the wastebasket on her way to the bathroom. Picking it up, she recognized a face from her childhood decorating the damn thing—Franklin D. Roosevelt himself, his cigarette in a long holder pointing at her from his grin.

"Allen," she wailed, turning the wastebasket to see each of its six sides on which, sure enough, as well as Roosevelt were Washington, Lincoln, Truman, Eisenhower and Kennedy.

"Well, Happy America to you," he said, laughing. "I see that Johnson and Nixon didn't make it. Hey, they're probably inside where they belong."

"Oh, I adore this place," she said, undressing.

In the bathroom she turned on the shower full blast, not giving a damn if water splashed all over the floor. Around and around she turned under the stinging hot needles that poured through her dusty hair. She used up all the measly bars of soap, rubbed herself dry with three bath towels which she then threw in the corner. As she lay next to Allen's breathing, he scratched his toenail along the calf of her leg, then pulled her head into the soft cushion of his neck.

They sat side by side in the big bed, sipping motel instant coffee, munching on sweet rolls and oranges. They tossed the peels into the Presidents' wastebasket and watched the "Today Show" on TV.

"Couldn't we just stay here all day long?" Patricia asked.

"You're kidding, of course," Allen said.

"Yes, but wouldn't it be nice?"

"Patricia!" he said, jumping out of bed and marching to the bathroom.

He must lose some weight, she thought with a sigh.

"We're going on a picnic," Dawn announced as they puffed up to the cabin door and collapsed on the grassy slope.

"Marvelous," Allen said, "but let an old man rest a minute, okay?"

"Sure, no hurry. But you've got to meet Josiah. He's a poet. You'll like him, Daddy. And Ellen. And Star."

"How do we get there?" Allen said, sitting up.

"We walk, take turns on Queenie if you want," Dawn said, nodding her head toward a nice little donkey who stood over by the bathtub looking at them shyly.

Patricia had not brought any of her sketching things or even a camera, though her reason was unclear now as she brought up the rear of the strange procession twisting through the Indian country, up and down, across iris fields, into deep woods, through marshes. She must have been mad, she thought, as she watched photogenic Queenie, barely visible beneath Allen's bulk, stepping along the path with her tiny hoofs. The baby, pressed to Dawn's back in a bright woven sling, swayed with her rhythm. Barnie led them at a good, steady clip, identifying herbs, trees, flowers along the way.

Without warning they came upon a cabin, even smaller than Dawn and Barnie's, as they emerged from the dark woods into a sunny clearing next to a creek. Josiah, a loose jointed lad, was splitting wood.

"Allen, Trish, sure nice to meet you," he said, smiling sleepily and hunkering down on his heels. This seemed to be the signal for all of them to sit on the ground. He reached in his shirt pocket for his supplies, rolled a joint, lit up, passed it around, then held his arms out for the baby.

"Hey, little moon child, come on over here."

They cuddled, crowed, rolled on the ground. A couple of joints went round and round, and eventually the procession moved on, enlarged now by Josiah, a goat and kid that he was taking to Ellen. An exchange, he said, for the use of her four–wheel drive. Had to do with some work on the road because of winter storms. His melodious voice lilted up and down and Patricia's head floated miles above her feet that walked softly, oh so softly, through the tiniest wildflowers she had ever seen. Her eyes, all–seeing, followed this path of flowers to Nadya's place. A lazy, lovely name, Nadya, rolling around in Patricia's head. And the woman matched the name. Smiling through half–closed lids, she unfolded her limbs and rose from the faded army blanket spread beneath a madrone tree.

"Well, hi there," Nadya said, then squatted by an outdoor fire and poked some sticks under a kettle.

Could that be Peter Pan jumping from a tree? Or Mowgli? About seven years old, Patricia thought, bare to the waist, and unmistakably a boy, the way he moved, despite the pigtail down his back. A younger child, a girl, stood naked, thumb in mouth, staring. Patricia longed to wash and brush the matted curls, settle down to playing house. She'd scrub and bleach the dingy clothes that hung on a line stretched between two trees, sweep the steps of the higgledy–piggledy hut...

"Want a joint?" Nadya said.

"Yeah, yeah, a joint," the Peter Pan boy yelled as he ran to the hut.

"Thank you, Zack," Nadya said when he brought her a cough drop tin and a package of cigarette papers.

Josiah folded Nadya into his arms and kissed her on the mouth. Had Patricia been mistaken about his homosexuality? She'd ask Allen. But now Allen slumped off the donkey's back and sank down beside Nadya, looking at her dirty feet.

"Hey, honey, you okay?" Nadya asked.

"Allen?" Patricia asked, running to him and looking into his far–away eyes.

"Just tired, a little faint," he said, lying in the dust. "Maybe some coffee..."

"Or tea? I got some camomile right here," Nadya said, and she and Dawn knelt by the fire to fix it.

"Better?" Patricia asked, pressing the cup to his lips.

"Wow, yeah," he said in a minute. "Funny, must have been the pot. Can we just sit awhile?"

And so they lounged under the trees for half an hour, drinking tea, smoking.

"Okay, let's go on this picnic!" Allen finally ordered like an aging patriarch.

"Now don't you cry, Gina," Nadya said, pulling a dress over the child's head, "we're going on a picnic! Come on, Zack, we're going on a picnic! Put the dope away now, baby."

Nadya trailed along with Patricia at the end of the line.

"Have you lived here long?" Patricia asked.

"Couple of years. Sure beats selling dope in New York City."

"Yes, I guess it would."

"You live in L.A.?"

"Hollywood, yes."

"Really? I was there once. Weird place," Nadya said, glancing at Patricia with a beautiful, condescending smile. Then she ran ahead in her bare feet, her long cool dress billowing out behind her, leaving Patricia feeling old and irrelevant at the end of the line.

Her stomach suddenly growled with hunger. A festering blister on her heel had apparently burst, leaving a burning sore to rub against the inside of her tennis shoe with every step. Her jeans were too tight, and Allen was getting off the donkey again. Stuck in a nightmare with feet that couldn't seem to run, a cotton–filled head that couldn't find the answer to a riddle, she struggled to get to Allen who lay in the grass.

"Just a little faint," he said as she curled against him.

"We can go back, you know," she said. But she knew they would go on and on. The baby cried again. Dawn nursed him again. Helplessly caught in the repetitive patterns of this odyssey, Patricia knew they would have to follow the meandering trail to the end.

"It's just a little way, Daddy. Around the next bend, beyond those fir trees up ahead."

"Well, come on, let's go," Allen said, climbing onto Queenie. With cautious optimism Patricia walked behind Allen and Queenie through the cool fir grove. But when she saw the bleak tarpaper shanty she stifled a sob. Queenie stepped deftly through an abandoned vegetable garden, avoiding broken bottles and strands of rusted wire, toward the two laughing girls, Ellen and Star. Patricia followed.

"Well, it's about time, you guys," one of them said.

"We've made a carob cake with brandy!" the other said.

Suddenly all the messes, including her own in the motel room and the lumber barons' on the battered hillside, made Patricia feel ill, disgusted with the human race. But Allen slid off the donkey again and sank into the debris. It was Allen, not she, who retched, then rolled onto his back, clutching at his ribs. She fell on her knees beside him.

"Hey, Ellen, you got anything but cake? How about some chicken soup? Allen here's feeling crummy," Barnie said.

Star hurried to Allen, pushing Patricia aside. "Go, scat!" she hissed at all of them. "Go on, eat some cake or something." She unbuttoned Allen's shirt. "Okay, honey, just relax now," she murmured, her ear against his hairy chest. "I'm a nurse, least I used to be. You're Dawn's Daddy, and that's good enough for me," she soothed, cradling his head in her lap. "You guys fix a stretcher out of something, and get ready to run with it, you dig?" she yelled.

For years afterwards Patricia would have a recurring dream in which a glimpse of that crazy return trip to civilization was vivid—herself running behind Barnie and Josiah who seemed to fly on their bare feet with the stretcher between them; Allen's large body jouncing like a sack of meal; the baby crying in jerky sobs as Dawn ran with him on her back; Nadya and Zack and Gina with vacant eyes, tripping along the path; and finally the whole bizarre group piling into Dawn's VW bus.

"You did just right, Miss," the doctor said respectfully, just as though Star were dressed in a crisp cotton dress instead of filthy jeans.

"Thanks, Doc. It was obvious he was having a heart attack."

"Oh no. Exhaustion, anemia perhaps. But not a heart attack, I'm happy to report."

Giddy with relief, Patricia was suddenly overwhelmed with affection for this odd little country doctor and all these friends of Dawn's.

"Well, sure he's exhausted, living in L.A.," Nadya drawled.

"Needs to be outdoors more," Josiah said to the sky as he leaned against the door jamb.

Dawn sat on the doorstep, nursing the baby.

"Oh shit!" Barnie swore to no one in particular.

"Can I see him now, Doctor?" Patricia asked.

"Of course, but just you, and keep it calm."

"Oh thank you. Yes, I'll be very quiet. Now all you children just wait for me, hear? I'll treat you to hamburgers."

"Remarkable family," the doctor commented as they walked down the green hallway, and she almost giggled.

"Well, really, they're not exactly family. Just by marriage. Just friends. I mean Dawn, the one with the baby, she's my step–daughter, and the others, well..."

"That's all right, Ma'am. Anyway, they're mighty good friends, I'd say. Now your husband needs a good rest for a few days. Probably had a little pot, eh?"

Friends? No. More like those intense relationships that develop on one's travels. That's what it had been, an excursion into a world she'd never see again. But Dawn and the baby...? Patricia, sitting at her desk in Hollywood, looking out over Laurel Canyon, finally brought her attention back to her letter. "The flight was okay," she wrote to Dawn, "but Allen must still take it easy. Apparently it *was* his heart, an 'incident' they call it...and I don't know when we'll be able to pick up the car. Maybe in the summer..."

When summer came, however, little crises in the lives of Joanie, Ben, Angel, and even Joe, added to her secret anxiety over Allen's lethargy. She forgot about the car, except in dreams. Nightmares in which her hand stroked the gleaming yellow surface of the Jaguar's hood, or in which she sank into the smell and feel of old leather. Disgusting visions that woke her in cold sweats. She took showers in the middle of the night to rid herself of the distortions, then crawled back into bed to watch Allen's sleeping profile.

"No damn funeral," he told her shortly before he died in August. So no reason for Dawn to come, and the ties between the two women, always tenuous, shrivelled, now, in spite of themselves. No more than a gossamer thread remained, destined to blow away in the winds of winter, leaving only memories of blue iris in the meadows, a nameless child with eyes like shiny pebbles. And a yellow Jaguar.

Jane Strong

Voyage

My father
rides with us on the old raft
balanced on the weathered boards
between two buoyant oil drums
Lightheaded and empty
they hold us afloat.

My father
stays between us on the flat deck
My brother rides the forward
drum, I'm on the aft, both
of us armed with wooden paddles
from an old canoe.

My father
is silent; we pole slowly
crossing the sandbar, gold
streak in the gray–green waters,
moving toward the cobalt blue
of the greater depths.

My father
passenger not captain, ignores
our awkward sculling with paddles
not intended for such a task
as we slow, . . . we slow, . . .
we grow becalmed.

My father
your ride is run. Slowly we slide
the bleached and altered bones
of my father's life into the
curling waters at our feet.

My father
is gone to the depths
of the great waters, to rest
on the rippled golden floor.
We retrace our wake
over a lake brimming
with mystery.

Jane Strong

Love in a Foreign Language

Elizabeth hears the wooden gate crash open against the plaster archway and bang shut again with enough force to drop the metal latch into its slot. Her head rings with the sound of boots echoing across the flagstones, their metal tips making distinct scraping sounds like sparks struck from a flint. She moves silently from the kitchen across the cold stone of the foyer to peer out the grillwork openings near the heavy wooden door.

The stocky figure of the young Greek strides through the garden rattling the red carnations in their pots as he passes. Doves, jarred from the ancient dovecote tower by the slammed gate, stream across the sky above his head. Oblivious as a young bull, he plows through the landscape as if he owns it, while behind him the white–washed village sprawls down the rocky hillside to the sea.

She shrinks back from the grillwork although he has not looked up. She has a momentary impulse to run and hide, to turn back the clock to some innocent early beginning. He stamps across the stone deck to the front door. There is nothing to do but open to his knock.

"Hello, Nico. It's five o'clock. You're right on time." Greeks are not prompt. It's a village joke. She smiles.

He does not smile, or touch her, or laugh, or take her in his arms. He only stands in the doorway and looks at her. He wears his usual blue jeans and blue denim jacket, America's gift to the young Greeks, she thinks, and the heavy black shoes that no American boy would wear. Under his blue fisherman's cap, his black hair curls over his ears and across his forehead, leaving his dark eyes in deep shadow, his face cloudy and stern.

"How are you?" she says inanely.

He is silent. Today his face is that of a stranger.

How can this male act at one moment like a man and the next like a child, like a brat in one of her second grade classes back home, only worse because there she was in charge and knew how to handle things, but here she is all at sea.

"Come in the kitchen. I'm washing dishes." She has been feeling uneasy all day, as if the air were charged with storm. The familiar chore will soothe her and give her time to think. She walks ahead of him, her back exposed, cold, as if there were a hole in her dress. At the sink, she busies herself, aware of him out of the corner of her eye. He merely leans against the wall, not smoking, doing nothing. She almost wishes he would help himself to wine without asking, something which usually annoys her.

"Would you like some retsina?" He nods, but it is clear he doesn't care one way or another. She is pouring the wine slowly from the heavy wicker–covered demijohn into two squat glasses when he says:

"You have good times last night?" Wine spills.

"Oh, all right," she says lightly, taking the natural sea sponge that she bought from the sponge vendor in Athens and sopping up the pool of spilled wine. She tries to think but all she can think of is the time he got so angry when she playfully slapped at him with the sponge. Don Moore was there having a drink with them and they had all been laughing about something, until the teasing slap. Instantly Nico's face had gone dark red with fury. She had apologized but he was deeply offended. Because another man was there, an American? Who knows why?

Elizabeth squeezes out the sea sponge, watching the red stain bleed into the white sink. "Last night I met an American woman and we have the same birthday!" More or less. The woman was just thirty and Elizabeth is thirty–three. Nico is nineteen. He says twenty. Not that he cares that she is so much older, nor does she care when they are alone, but in public it's not quite the same. She rattles on:

"So we decided to celebrate our birthdays, and a group of us went—" But Nico isn't listening.

In the sudden silence his words are loud. "You go home alone last night?"

The faint turpentine fragrance of the retsina meets her nostrils as she sips and pretends not to understand. "You mean did the group come back here for a drink? No, after the taverna, she went to her pension, and—"

He whips it away. "One boy come home with you last night?"

She looks at the sunlight filtering through the window pane to break apart in a glass jar of flowers on the windowsill. All the stems have their backs broken, bent out of shape by the beveled edges of the curved glass. She moves it out of the sun, inhales the piercing sweetness of jasmine, and says:

"That's really none of your business."

Back at the dishpan full of soapy water, she begins to wash a glass plate that is already clean. A headache is beginning. Perhaps a slight hangover accounts for it.

Boots grate against stone. "You sleep alone last night?"

Glass slips from her soapy hands. She imagines it breaking and cutting her, the dishwater going red with her blood while he just stands there ignoring it, bearing down with questions.

"Answer me. You sleep alone?"

She lets out the breath she has been holding. "Sleeping?" Her voice is off pitch. "No one spent the night here if that's what you're asking." Like a child lying with the literal truth, she thinks.

His voice is the color of steel. "I know one boy come home with you for sleep!"

She looks up, her hands still in the water. "If you think you know, why do you ask?"

He glares. "Answer me for truth. One boy come here with you for sleep? Yes or no." There is no inflection in his voice. It has never been like that before.

Oh God, I've made a mess of things, she thinks, pretending to give the dishwashing her full attention. How has it got to this? If she could just go back in time to when it was all a new sensual experience so different from the dull responsibilities and possibilities at home. To the time when everything was offered to her, a marvelous gift with no strings attached, both of them exploring pleasure on a hedonistic holiday with no rules and no limits. What had happened?

"What I do or don't do is not your business. It is my business."

There is a crash. Where has he gone? She rushes to the foyer, expecting to see what smashed, but there is nothing. He stands at the wall. Evidently he has hit it with his hand and several small *lepta* coins which had lined the sill have fallen to the stone floor. The sound still rings.

Bull–like, his head comes up and he looks steadily at her from under his eyebrows.

"I no drink last night. You lucky. Otherwise you be dead!"

"What did you say?!"

He nods. "Everybody with hands for like that!" He takes a pose, arms bent, wrists crossed, as if arranged in a coffin. Somehow she knows it is the Greek gesture for death.

She feels frozen in place like a statue. Cold air filters past the grill, seeps down the damp stone walls to the rough–cut marble floor of this English–built house she is renting, more elegant but colder than a Greek house. Chill rises from the stone, numbs her legs, crawls under her skirts... It reminds her of the dank glacial vaults under the Bridge of Sighs in Venice, a dungeon where once prisoners were chained in bitter cold, forgotten... She jerks her mind sharply to heel.

"Don't be silly. That's nonsense. You can't talk that way." Firmly, she returns to the kitchen and wipes up the counters, rinses the enamel dishpan and hangs it on a nail. He follows.

"I no drink last night. Otherwise I think you no be here." His voice is deadly calm.

This idea that to be drunk permits you to be wild, violent, out of control, a monster, the school teacher thinks, is so prevalent here, especially among the young studs, young males on the prowl, looking for battle. Surely in Athens it's more civilized. Does he really mean that if he had been drunk, he would have killed—? Deliberately she focuses her mind on domestic tasks. She has never been so thorough. She must be calm, matter–of–fact, ordinary. How much does he know, she wonders, as she fluffs out the sponge and sets it in its dish.

"Cigarettes?" she says. "Behind you on the shelf. Help yourself." Her tone is light but she thinks: if anger came to him so easily for a little thing like a sponge...

He jerks the box of Papastratos, shooting one cigarette up to his mouth and spilling a second on the floor, which he retrieves, and places in his shirt pocket. From the small box of wooden matches, he needs three before he gets a good light. Always he strikes too hard, breaking their necks, knocking off their heads too short for use. It is so typical of him.

At once, without warning, she is swept by a gust of desire. Her flesh begins to prickle and she feels the familiar stirring like a beast stretching, as it wakes... Part of her wants to forget everything else and simply live in the moment. Receive life like a piece of music, giving way to it, becoming totally a part of it, pure feeling, sensation, no consequences... she mustn't look at him. She concentrates on feeling nothing. In a moment it will go away if she does nothing about it. All the years at home of being calm and sensible will give her direction and she will deal with this in a manner that will be acceptable to society. Communication, arbitration, resolution of conflict, all those admirable things will come into play. Whatever that means. With Olaf at home there were never any of these situations. Olaf was quiet and predictable. Reliable Olaf, and she couldn't remember what he looked like. She takes a deep breath.

"Do you want to talk about it?" she says.

"Yes."

"There's a little more retsina?"

"Okay."

Elizabeth refills the glasses and sets them on a wooden tray with a dish of Greek olives and an ashtray. She starts toward the living room. The big front window, fine on hot days, is now closed and though she has stuffed the cracks around the wooden frames with newspapers, the raw winds continue to blow through. Drafts are everywhere. Who would have believed Greece would be so cold? She could close the heavy wooden shutters but then it would be dark as well. The bedroom, with the tiny petrol heater, is the room she lives in. That and the kitchen. They go into the bedroom.

It is a mistake. Too late she remembers that she had intended to make the bed before Nico arrived. He is staring at it as if he had never seen it before. Involuntarily, she too looks at the rumpled bedclothes, seeing what he imagines. As casually as possible she pulls the spread over the disorderly bed, as she motions him to sit in one of the two rattan chairs. She sets the tray on the low stool in front of him, a miniature coffee table, and turns it around so the olives are near him.

She takes a cigarette and sits down in the other rattan chair. She has been quitting but now is not the time. Here no one quits smoking. They are always offering, taking, asking for, lighting, smoking cigarettes. A land of voracious mouths, eating, drinking, talking, making love... The heater sputters in the silence, its coils showing faintly red.

Finally Nico breaks the silence.

"How long this boy stay last night? He sleep here all night?"

"No," she says, expelling smoke. "He stayed about an hour and then left." Blue smoke curls upward, drifting toward the high ceiling, giving the room an unreal air. The heater's glow is as cold as an artificial fire made of red lights on composition logs.

"You like this too much," he says.

Yes, she thinks in surprise, yes, that's true.

"You feel love?" he asks quietly.

"No. Nothing special." It was nothing at all, really, a passing bid for independence, for control over her life again. Now, she wasn't sure why she did it.

He looks at her in silence, nods several times, speaks quietly. "I think it be good I no drink last night. I no be drunk." He nods again.

"Of course, Nico, you must realize that we each have our own lives. We don't own each other. I don't like this possessive attitude you've suddenly been showing. I really don't like it!"

He continues as if she hadn't spoken. His tone is calm and conversational:

"If I be drunk, I come in, get knife from drawer in kitchen, come in bedroom, kill first him, then you, then myself!"

Silence spreads around his words like ripples in water around a hurled stone. She feels as if she had been laughing hysterically and suddenly stopped, as if a hand had been placed over her mouth. At this moment in the kitchen drawer the knives are lying neatly in their narrow slots, all sizes, made of English steel and very sharp. It was one of the things she had admired when she first moved in.

Winter chills the room. In this village by moonlight the whitewashed paths and steps even look like snow. She feels as if she were moving through that cold, trackless world, lost, weak, almost overwhelmed with the desire to lie down in the snow and sleep. So easy. So simple....

She rouses herself. "But you didn't come in."

"No."

"What made you think he was here?"

"I see him."

"You followed me?" cries Elizabeth, stung to life. "You spied on me?"

"No. I was here last night."

"You were here? Where?"

"Outside."

"What do you mean? In the garden? Outside my door?"

"In the road, outside the gate. When I see the light go out, I be crazy!" He smokes his cigarette down till he nearly burns his fingers. There is no filter tip. She holds her breath against the dank acrid smell of the tobacco dregs.

"You'd better tell me about it," she says at last.

He peels off his jacket and gestures while he talks. His blue work shirt is rolled up tight above the bulging biceps which come from hauling in nets of fish.

"Last night I no drink nothing," Nico insists. This fact seems to amaze him. "I don't know why. I no feel good. I be home for to eat. Later I be with one tourist man, Don."

"Go on."

"Yes, okay. We go *cafenion*. Don say, what you have? I say, I have one ouzo—you know I like ouzo?"

Yes, she knew, but she found it too strong to offer it to him very often.

"But I say, no ouzo. I have coffee. Don say, why you no drink? I say, don't know. Don't want. Maybe I feel sick. Later maybe I eat." He munches on an olive, spits the seed into his hand. Elizabeth pushed the ashtray nearer and he drops the seed into it.

"Later we go to Marko's to drink. Don order one bottle beer, two glasses. I say no. I want *nero*. Water, only water. Don say, drink his beer. I no want. Don say why? I say, *thim berazzi!* Never mind, you know?"

Yes, she knows *thim berazzi* means 'never mind'. She hears it all the time. It means something very Greek, she thinks, though whether it's fatalism, or stoicism, or 'forget it, it's not important', she's not sure.

"Why I no drink last night?"

Why was Don trying to get him to drink? "I don't know," she says. "Why do you think?"

"Maybe the God say no drink!"

Elizabeth shivers in the cold. Without taking her eyes off him, she reaches behind her for a sweater. "Then you came into the Club?" she prompts.

He nods. "Don say you drink something now? I say okay, one vermouth, make me sleep. But I no sleep."

Sweet vermouth, she thinks, pink and cloying. How he loves sweet things. "I saw you come in but I didn't see when you left," she says. "Did you see me?"

He shrugs and she knows he did. Probably left the room the minute he saw her.

"Go on."

"Later I be at Don's for cigarette. I say, I go home now. But I go for a walk. I no feel sleepy. I walk...I walk..."

"Yes?" Something odd is happening to his voice. As if he had left a path and were beginning to stumble about in the undergrowth.

"...past your house. I think I see light. You say: no come tonight. But I think, maybe I come, just to your door, just say hello..."

In a city, Elizabeth is thinking, these things don't happen. In a city, there is some privacy.

"Then I see you in door with one boy, go in, turn on more light. My hand be on gate, ready to come. But I say, wait!"

"Yes?" Why hadn't she seen him out there? Why hadn't she been prepared for this?

"I think maybe he come out in minute. He no come out. I see more light. I think, maybe he have coffee, something first, then go. I be angry. I wait. Later I see light go on in bedroom..."

She holds her breath.

"I watch light in bedroom. I feel bad. But I say, wait, maybe have coffee in bedroom because for cold in living room, wait..."

She sits very still, waiting.

After a moment he continues, voice ragged. "But then I see light in bedroom go out. I be crazy! I be very very angry. I think I go first, smash glass, come in..."

"Break the glass of the living room window?" She thinks how easy it would be, how she never bothers with the heavy shutters.

"Yes, I break glass, come kitchen, get knife, come bedroom, kill everybody."

Such a thing could happen, Elizabeth thinks dully.

"If I be drunk last night, now all be dead."

Silence spreads in the cold room.

Elizabeth remembers when she was a child a large black chow, with a reputation for attacking children, which she had to pass each day coming home from school. She would wonder about dogs and the smell of fear. She would force herself to talk to the dog in calm tones, but she always wondered whether the dog smelled her fear anyway and was laughing at her pretenses. She would keep her hands high and out of the way, carrying her books, and move at a slow steady pacing, talking all the while. When she reached home she would go to the bathroom and vomit...

"Did you come into the yard?"

"No! Many times I put my hand on gate to come in. I say no. I say wait. I be very angry. I be crazy! I talk to myself. I wait."

"You waited but you did not come in."

He nods.

"You were strong."

"Later I no be strong." Nico says softly. "I be very weak. I shake. My hands shake. I can do nothing."

Elizabeth looks at his strong hands, hard–used, hard–working hands, older than his years.

"Sometimes I laugh, laugh at myself…"

"You laugh at yourself?" She is amazed.

"Yes. I say, Nico, this tourist woman make bad time for you. I be very crazy. Sometimes I go to gate. I touch handle, I think I come in. Then I say no, I think that no a good idea. I stay in street. I smoke many cigarette. I feel sick. Later, sometimes, I think, I cry. Later I cry."

"Oh, Nico! But it was wrong of you to follow me."

He turns his head toward her voice, but looks past her as if he were seeing how it was and trying to find words in her language to explain it to her. "Then I go," he said.

"Where? Home? Nothing was open that late, was it?"

He explains he went to Don's, stayed to smoke two cigarettes, but said nothing of what had happened. ("I smile. I look happy.") Then he left, wandered down to the windswept waterfront where he spent the rest of the night in the open, perched on a cafe chair, huddled against the outside plaster wall of the tiny Fishermen's Church. Damp cold came easily through his two sweaters and his denims, and the waterfront winds tugged at his billed yachting cap jammed low on his forehead. He smoked all his cigarettes, at the last lighting one from the stub of the one before because he had run out of matches. Once someone came by and offered him shelter but he refused; after that he saw no one. Sometimes there was a little rain; or perhaps it was only wind–borne spray from the sea a few meters away.

She could picture the dark figure on the open quay, huddled against an igloo of a church, blue–white in the thin moonlight, buffeted by the blast of wind which always seemed to scour the waterfront, even at midday.

Outside, darkness is falling from the sky and welling up out of the sea, turning the houses through golden white to pale blue to bluish gray. From the window, past his head, she can see a sliver of the village beyond her wall.

"Poor Nico. I'm sorry you had such a bad night."

He stares steadily at her. "At first, never mind. We play, have good times. At first, is good, yes?" She agrees. He nods, smiling a smile that seems to hurt his face. She starts to speak but he gestures. "Now, is different. Now is too much sadness, too much love. Now I have trouble in my heart. You understand? No, I think not."

Inside her, the teacher thinks 'heart trouble' and is oddly touched, but in deeper layers, she is troubled and confused. Part of her wants to agree, to understand, but part sees the need for control. She takes a different tack.

"You were very strong last night, Nico. A man, not an angry child." Her voice sounds stiff in her ears.

"Yes, I be strong." She hears his breathing in the almost dark room.

"There's a little retsina left. Why don't we kill it?"

In a plaster niche in the bedroom, there is a small lamp, which she gets up to turn on. The room jumps out at them. "I'll be right back." She returns carrying a tray on which are two full glasses of wine and a plate of bread and cheese. "I'm proud of you for being so strong," she says.

"Yes. I come grown. I have years."

Years? She looks at him suspiciously. "Just how old are you really? Nineteen?"

"Yes," he says after pausing a fraction of a sentence.

"No, you're not. Eighteen? Seventeen?"

"I be eighteen soon. Why you ask?"

"Seventeen!" My God! "Are you even seventeen?"

"Uh–yes, seventeen."

"You're not even seventeen!"

"Almost seventeen. For true."

"Sixteen!" Good Lord, what was she doing involved with this unpredictable hot–headed boy? After all her plans, her promises to herself... little more than a child. "That's terribly young!"

"In your country is young." Nico says firmly. "Is not young here."

Elizabeth feels as if she had pushed off from shore on a sunny day in one of those little orange fishing skiffs she has seen upturned along the wharf, and then suddenly one of those Greek storms had blown up, without warning the sky had gone dark, the sea had become violent, and now she is lost.

Nico has reverted to his theme: why did he not drink the night before. He always acts as if his drinking is pure chance, something that happens to him beyond his control, she thinks. Once it had happened, this phenomenon of drinking, he was not responsible for what deed of violence might ensue.

"Listen," she says. "Think how terrible it would have been for everyone if you had done such a thing! For your family. For your mother—" Mothers were so important in Greece—"for your mother to think that her son...? The dishonor—?" how could she say it?—"the bad name would hurt very much, wouldn't it?"

He nods.

"Bad for your family and friends. Bad for your village, your people. Bad for all Greece."

He agrees. "Bad for everyone."

She shivers. "And my family, Nico, imagine how bad it would have been for my mother and father."

He nods politely. Her family is remote.

"My friends, other Americans. Imagine how they would feel about Greece? A savage country. Bad."

"Very bad," Nico agrees with surprising good humor. He gives her a cigarette and lights one for himself. He looks at her from under his dark eyebrows and says something. She doesn't understand.

"What?"

He says the word slowly, and grins. "Primitive!"

"Look," she says angrily, "I am much older than you—"

"*Thim berazzi!*"

Never mind, never mind, she was sick of hearing it. That grin of his that made him look like a naughty seven year old from one of her classes. "Listen to me. This is nothing to fool about. Someday you will marry and have children—"

"I don't care! Why you say this?"

"Because I go back to my own country soon."

"Yes," he says quietly. "I know. I feel sad. No speak of that."

"Yes, but don't you see? This girl who visits your mother, what's her name?"

"*Thim berazzi!*" His gesture is impatient.

"Or some other girl, you know. Don't you see how different our lives are?" She licks her dry lips.

"So?"

"So what you do is your business. What I do is mine. We don't belong to each other." Her throat feels scarred.

He stands, makes a movement with his mouth as if to spit out an olive pit.

"Nico, listen. We are friends. *Filos*." Or was that 'lovers'?

He nods, looking down at her.

"We will never forget each other—" To her surprise she understands that this is true and the knowledge confuses her. He stands in front of her, rests his hand on her shoulder. She looks up at him. "But we lead our separate lives. You do understand?"

"Yes." At that moment he makes her feel that she is a child and he is the ancient, mature one, product of a long history, the seer, the father. His hand rests heavily on her shoulder.

"We understand each other," she whispers.

"Yes."

He is looking at her with such concentration and pressing so hard on her shoulder, that she feels unable to rise. But a pain, which has been hovering behind her eyes this last hour, begins to climb sharply. "I'm sorry, but I'm getting one of those headaches..."

"You come sick?"

"Yes, I—"

"You want me stay? You want me go?"

"You better go. I should sleep."

"Okay, I go now." He taps her lightly on the shoulder.

"But you be careful, eh?"

Elizabeth expels a long breath. "Oh yes, I will. I'll take a couple of aspirins—"

"Never mind that. You be careful. No again one boy come home with you for sleep! In your country, I don't care. But in my country, very bad!"

Headache and nausea blur in the chill of the foyer as she goes to the door with him. "We'll talk later," she mumbles. She holds the front door open for him.

His smile is full of sweetness. "Next time, I be crazy. I be drunk. God no be with me. You be careful, eh?"

The heavy wooden door slams shut behind him like the door of a tomb. Boots echo through the garden. The gate bangs open and shut and she imagines the white doves streaming across the darkened sky.

I must hide the knives, she thinks.

Mary L. Hanner

The Spring Offensive

The war was before we were
born or old enough to climb
to the place where a house
stores dreams, helmets
with holes, belt buckles
and roses wrapped in rotting
peau de soie. When we
chose sides our sieges were
behind worn chairs and winter
coats, beneath a row of gas masks
impaled on rafters by dark
shafts of afternoon. And in the
game one day we put them on,
these windows mocking green May.
"No one has to
die this time," we promised in
child voices behind that glass
where mustard gas still
smells of apple blossoms.

Mary L. Hanner

Demonia

I am seized
by your perfume
of fear. It leaps
at me from hallways
where we escape
each other's eyes.
The fragrance startles.
It fills my head
with the ancient
pheronome of an offense,
some uncleaness, interpreted
momentarily by a flare
of nostrils. Chimera devils
rise on dizzy aromatics.
Their faces are familiar
at the edges, like bedtime
stories gone bad.
Banshees and medusas cry and
curl around the air displaced
by knotted muscles.
Our hearts rally, engorge
and skip a beat.
The hall is dark
and close between these walls,
and when we touch shoulders
as we pass you will
smell terror
on my breath
like an old garlic charm

Mary L. Hanner

Delivery

When the children leave
and he does too
she notices

that silence has a sound
within these rooms,
peculiar and haunting

fragments of a voice
gurgled in pale yellow water,
but salty.

This little sound disturbs her
second cup of coffee
taken with cream

as one of those tunes
that clutches at the edges
of the mind.

And the sound grows.
It shakes her windows and tears
at her poppy colored robe,

until, naked and shivering,
she spills out on white sheets
this new, bloody being.

She thinks she will never forget
that sound. One day
standing alone by the sea

something hot will burn her cheek
like being touched by an angel,
but salty.

Mary L. Hanner

City Poem at Night

The city of darkened windows
suspends a thousand window
washers in leather straps with
double catches. They hang
above the city making slow circles
in that halo of ammonia and benzene rings.

A night lady comes, her carbon
face pressed hard to the street.
Neon sequins spill across her
black shawl, and the city moves
to dim reflections through
its dirty panes.

Mongrel dogs, yellow dogs
with yellow teeth, snarl and tear
at bystanders in raincoats. They
toss coins to the lady, but
no one buys their way in the dark.
They are devoured in alleys,
in a hundred byways where saliva
and blood make stale rivers
along urban ledges.

At dawn the poisonous haze creeps
over windows like a finger smudge.
The dogs are quiet and filled,
and the lady collects her shawl.
A window washer, awakened from dreams
by light, releases the catches and
slips in silence to the street below.

Mary L. Hanner

Debut

Suppose you do not enter the room
calmly but in a jangle of bones
and snarled hair. And the face
in the gilded mirror on the opposite
wall is not your face. That face is
rouged and quiet. Notice how
the eyes round down too much
to be yours. And because you are
not calm your head won't balance
over your hips. You stumble.
And when you fall your legs are
oak fence posts, your knees are
broken and still they do not bend.
Suppose an unexpected door opens
and you do not enter the room
calmly. Suppose the room is
not a room.

Mary L. Hanner

Jeremiad

She spoke to the wind.
That isn't easy.
She hoped for some answer
to her whisperings
other than the neighbors'
who said she was crazy.

Not that she expected lightning
or hand writing in the sky,
but she found messages
from potato peelings
or dust curls under the bed
too difficult to decipher.

One day she got married
and settled down, and she
raised a number of fine sons,
except one had some difficulty
with the authorities.

She never mentioned whether
she got an answer.
I think she still
wanders in the garden
calling softly for Gabriel and Elijah.

Mary L. Hanner

Five Women:
Bicentennial Poem For San Jose 1777-1977

Five women wait in the morning,
gray and dim, for the bus beside
a concrete sea of flowers by design
and trees pruned into lollipops,
engineered relief from streets and
city buildings sunk in cemeteries.

1

One is old, brown and creased.
Her hair is blown across her face
where tears flowed for sons, tanned
sons who sprawled across her lap,
hungry for gold and the taste of
new milk, now gone. She wears her
story on her back, against the
cold and twists the fringes at
the edge into a dream as she would
have her daughters' hair, long
and black.

2

Another is not young, but waits
in printed voiles of butterfly wings.
Her hands are burled from garden
strings and guns and sons she made
for war. Their lean faces at

eighteen sit on the tv set
she watches. She was never young.
She wears her scars as silently
as penicillin that saved her
from the doctor's dirty hands.

3

A third, wearing calico and daisy
chains stolen from a garden wall,
names her babies by seasons and dances
to the music of a morning dove
mistakenly diverted from the fields.
As pliable as gold, she bends
her mind to ochre rainbows,
having noticed thunder.

4

The child is young with school
books and glen plaid skirts and
braids and eyes as blue as sins.
First born from the crayola
suburbs, she plays at jacks
and draws hopscotch on the
concrete walk with chalk. She
writes her name in cursive
and does not know her father's.

Our destinations are certain
as the sun, but if the bus
doesn't come, for awhile, I hope
the old one will tell her
stories and the sad one will sing
her songs of wars and sons.
The one who loves the sun and
wind might teach us how
to dance, how to wind the daisies
in our hair and how to play
at jacks. And the child will
lead us laughing through this
waking city's streets.

Maxine Zalkin

Warnings about Bath Water

This poem does have another name which you will
certainly be able to figure out
before the end of this page

the bath water in the white enamel pan with the dark
blue edge chipped black
here and there
the water somewhat cloudy–with–soap now
and full of a shining slippery fat pink clean baby laughing
and wiggling
and the mother taking the pan
the somewhat large oval pan something like a turkey
roaster
heavy for her to carry
and giving it a big toss toward the open window and out
flies water
cloudy soapy water in one whole splash with droplets
flying every which way
and out flies too a slippery pink wiggly heavier object
not the soap
the baby
Oh my god I've thrown out the baby she shrieks and runs
for the door
she picks up the still wiggling slippery pink and plump
but not now laughing
outraged baby who fortunately has landed upright on a
small plot of thick Kentucky
blue grass and she the mother is chagrined
whew her first impulse didn't turn out to be a final
statement
over the last late relations with her bubbling burbling baby

and the name of this poem is naturally
don't throw out the baby with the bath water but
she was the type who had to try things before she could
know
what words mean
even mean words and so the name of this poem might
have been
don't throw out the sayings with the wrath
(watch 'er)
at least until you know what they mean

How does tradition ever ever get handed down with words
or is it tradition
secret unintentional unmentionable tradition for mothers
to try at least once
when no one is watching
to throw the baby out
and is that why people hand down
to each new generation of daughters become mothers
the warnings about bath water
and laugh when they say it

Alice Wirth Gray

Welcome Home, Barney Corey

My name is Barney Corey. I'm free again and white and twenty–one last week and they let me out on my birth-day and I'm going to do–de–do–do you. I've got a brand new shirt and I'm going to do you dirt. They let me go be-cause they love me and they said, "Take the bus straight. Your mother's expecting you and she'll notify us if you don't appear by noon." Mom says, "It's good to see you. Now you're here, you can feed the cats. I need to get out for a bit." She starts throwing stuff in a canvas bag. "You watch out, they just didn't want the fuss to transfer you to the Adult Authority. I told em I'd let you use my old Merc to check out jobs. YOU BUST SOMETHING, YOU NEVER COME IN HERE AGAIN, GET IT? Don't tell em I ain't here, I'm supposed to watch you good. Don't forget to feed the cats. There's four of em now." She hops on a bus to Harrah's Stateline, she loves those slot machines. Mom has always trusted me. I put my woolly gloves in my pocket and go downstairs to see who's around and there's nobody. I been gone a while. But say, see what's new, the station for the Rapid Transit, and hell, I like to ride as much as Mom so I get on and go north I think to the end of the line but it gets to freaky Berkeley, it ducks down under-ground and this little boy, I don't like riding through the grave. Soon as I figure how to get off the thing, I get out and start walk-ing. There's a big empty space says BUSINESS PLAZA but all there is is one shiny new drugstore, nothing else anywhere. What I need, I think, is a note book so I go to "School Supplies Aisle 23" and see a real nice clipboard I wouldn't of thought of and a pack-age of paper. A pencil I already got, I'm supposed to circle jobs in the want ads. I carry my stuff past this blondie behind the counter, she's wide as a bed, big dumb pale blue eyes, looks like she's thought of a question to ask like "Hey, aren't you gonna pay for those?" I give her a sweet smile and say, "You'd look cute with your nose cut up the side and curled, like you got a fried squid on your face." She looks like she forgot her question. Silly to let a girl work in a place so empty all alone, but the big drugger himself is probably there in the back asleep. I put the paper in a yellow–and–red plaid vinyl clipboard and watch the plasticrap blow up the street. I follow it and then walk on and on uphill. People get richer the higher you go, at least in California. In the Center a kid from Salvador told me down there the poor live uphill and their piss runs down on the rich, but then it's winter here when it's summer there, so maybe so. Halfway up this hill, they ain't rich, they ain't poor, they don't worry about me looking for em here. I go along real obvious with my clipboard and stop in front of every house and write down the address and what I see in the window, in this town mostly a lot of cruddy pictures. Any second I expect to run like hell, some old biddy yells "What the hell you think you're doing?" and I can run real good, I'm lean and I'm mean from Juvenile Hall. But like they say, Berkeley's real tolerant, room for all, or maybe just nuts. Or maybe these Levi's and this shirt they send me home in look better than a meter reader, maybe I look so nifty I'm the tax assessor's man, I'm the man from Gallup Poll, I'm the Nielson rating man, I'm Barney Corey. Then there's a house, I'm home free, go no farther, the tape deck backs up to the window, man–o–man–o–money, it sings equipment to the eyeballs. So I circle the address and strut official–like around the house. The garage is open, looks like it always is, but they forgot my ladder. The window's open to a bedroom. These are lovely trusting people, musical people, they're singing "Come in, Barney Corey, welcome, Barney, come in! Rob us, rape us, we love you!" Windows open nights is one thing: windows open days, those bozos love more than fresh air: they love ME. I love this town. I go back downhill four houses, I find an open garage got a ladder in it. So now I need a car. I head toward the BART station and lean against a lightpole to think. There's my lone old drugstore. It's five minutes of six and dark and cold and out comes an old guy and the same blondie, business is no good, they only got one salesgirl and the chief pillpusher hisself. He locks up, goodnight, goodnight, and goes off one way and she heads around behind the building. Me too. She's unlocked a dark blue

Cortina and opened the door. I grab her around the neck and squeeeeeze and then let loose a little. "Cool," she gurgles, "cool. Just let me breathe, please. Just let me breathe. Take what you want. Cool." I take the keys and push her down on her butt which ain't going to damage this one much. She's got her eyes all screwed up shut like she hurts and I wonder if she ever even looked at me, knows who I am. I say, "You should take the Rapid Transit, you pay a lot of taxes for it and you don't use it, this is God's punishment on you." I drive up the hill and park by the house with the stuff in it. No lights, no car in the garage, but still no ladder. I tritty–trot downhill to where there's new drawn curtains and old Pop's car is in the garage, but the door's still open and my ladder's there, ten feet long and no moving parts. I tote it uphill. They still invite me in. They love me, Barney Corey. I see the kids in the next house with their backs to me, watching TV, so close to the little box, it's bad for their gonads. I have this run–in with a climbing rose. If they think their rose is a match for my pretty new pants, they don't know Levi's, I should be an ad for em, the pants that raped the West. These folks don't keep up their property, their window sill's so rough and peeling, it wouldn't take a fingerprint, I didn't need to bring my gloves. I head downstairs, a real musician's pad, I see. What group's he with, I wonder? First I open the front door. I pull the speakers loose and sit the changer on top but I see these three guitars. One of em I can't get a grip on, the handle on the case is busted. So I stack the changer on the other two and there's this clarinet lying loose I can tuck under my arm. Then, this being Berkeley and them so musical, I think where do they keep the pot? Right there on the floor by the waterbed is a little chest like it might be Japanese. Bingo. So I stuff a bunch of joints in my pockets and get a bright idea with my knife to lay open the waterbed. Then I pick up my stuff and out to my car through the flood. My feet are soaked and it's real cold so I turn the heat on high and head for Mom's. No sweat, I'm back in San Leandro in the garage with the door down by eight–thirty loading stuff in the trunk of Mom's Merc. I go park the Cortina under the Lewelling offramp and walk back to Mom's. I think about the pot but I don't smoke it yet. I think about the phone but it's not ripe yet. I'm cool. I feed the cats.

Dumb Mom, she buys em Skippy, they don't like Skippy. They never did, not even this new one. They bitch, but I go to bed.

Five A.M. I get up. I got to go all the way to Alameda in the Merc, it won't go fast. Lots of dust, lots of cars, rows of old clothes, a mess to keep an eye on. At seven there's already a crowd setting up at the Flea Market. I haul a crate I got from Mom's garage I can set the changer and the clarinet on or hide em under, I see trouble. The guitars, no cop could tell they're hot. Musicians, off on a weekend gig somewheres, maybe nobody's rung the bell on me yet. I shouldn't of trashed the bed, it'll leak out the door and somebody notice before they would've. I'm Barney Corey, I'm smart, I'm strong, but I can be wrong.

Right away I get some action. Guy comes by lugging a big case, can't be a sax. A bassoon, I guess. He stops and eyes my changer. I say "You hot too?" He says, "Well, I don't personally blow bassoon myself. Wanna trade for the changer?" "Something nobody plays? Screw off, buddy." Jeez, he's so dumb, he cops a bassoon. I'm really nervous, too. The cops can't be so dumb they don't have nobody here? But it don't take but forty minutes, all my stuff is gone except for the clarinet. Sixty bucks for one guitar, forty–five for the other, I didn't see it had no strings, and I kinda mashed up the case with the Merc's trunk lid. Twenty bucks on the changer is all, everybody's got a good one since I went in. I don't know why everybody don't shop the flea markets, it just makes sense, they want big bargains. The clarinet, I start to get antsy, that freak with the bassoon was a Sign to me. Nobody blows clarinet either, one guy gives it a look asks how much. I say fifty bucks. The dumb crumb, instead of handing it over, he's in luck, he wants to give me lessons, he wants to argue. "You are weird, you know that? That's a Buffet, it's worth half a thou at least. Why are you selling?" I cross my eyes at him, stick my thumbs in my ears and waggle my fingers and blow bubbles at him. "Because you don't know HOW weird I am," I yell. He takes off pretty fast, but I wonder, could that be a cop? I head for the Merc quick and shove the clarinet into the ditch by the road.

Someday they'll bulldoze all this, build a real parking lot, get rid of all the dust.

I got one–hundred twenty–five bucks and a bunch of joints in the toe of the day bed. It looks like a beautiful weekend, Mom should have a waterbed, all the guys come through the Center since I went in they made it in waterbeds. I lie and smoke and it hits me right away, long time, no use. Three puffs and the phone is ripe. I call the Berkeley cops and say, "About that burglary on Oxford Street, those bastards are lying in their teeth. They fenced that stuff themselves, and they want the insurance. I know. I'm a neighbor, I saw it. And they're potheads, you know that? You should see the stash they got by the bed. Jeez, the whole street stinks at night, everybody knows it. It's a scandal to the jaybirds." I say it real fast and hang up. I feel pretty good. Maybe they'll get busted. I can dream, can't I? I really can dream, Mom don't get back till Tuesday. I'll find some of the old guys. I'll get a gun. I'll go to parties. I can't go to parties till I get a gun. It's nice just to let it drop out of my pocket, make a big noise on the floor. All the girls look, get real quiet, want the guys to take em home right away. I'm Barney Corey and I got to get a gun or a party's no fun. But I just lie around and smoke and feed the cats until Monday I think of something else fun to do. I get back on the BART train and grit my teeth when it ducks into the tunnel, Berkeley pays a lot of money to make the things run underground and it's so pretty it should be up in the air where they can be proud of it, not hide it in a wormhole. This really makes me mad. I get off at my drugstore and go in and there's my girl, she really sticks to it, give her credit. I thought she might of quit her job. She's got a turtleneck sweater and a scarf both around her neck, I guess I bruised her pretty good. Eyes just as wide, like she's got another question. I am really high and happy, almost horny but not so much. But *hungry*, the pot makes me feel my sweet tooth. "Hey, honey, hi. I come to tell you your car's parked under the Nimitz at Lewelling, you gonna need a new fanbelt." I come to hug you too, I start to think, but she's got the counter between me and her and her eyes look like she found her answer and she's gonna scream. I figure sure the druggist's got a gun by now, so I widen up my eyes like hers and stick my first fingers up my nose and bare my teeth like a werewolf and if I don't look like Dracula, I don't look like Barney Corey neither and it has the right effect. She gets real still and respectful, like girls should be and I pick up the biggest box of Valentine candy you ever saw and head for Rapid Transit. It's a great big heart with purple foil and gold lace and pink plastic flowers must weigh five pounds at least. Everybody's glad to see me on the train because I smile so nice and I'm happy and I've got such a big heart. I carry it pretty–side–out against my chest. All smiles, the world is: everyone loves a lover.

My shirt's new and my feet lift so nice and high and I got only one regret, I should've give the blondie a box of candy too, working in an empty lonesome place like that. Can't be a lover with no one to love. I'll go back tomorrow and fix it up. But I'll share this box with the cats in San Leandro. My fine big feet are so light, I'm in the middle of a clean wide beautiful street. I don't know where, but I don't care. I'm happy and I lie down in the street and it's soft as a cloud, like a waterbed. I open my heart and eat a little candy and spread a little around for the birds and roll some around, glittery little lumps like marbles and I roll around some with the candy and jeez, I'm happy and it's great to be free.

Mary Tolman Kent
The Berry Patch

She clings to a dream already no more than a mood, fading away as Poochie licks her hand and her throbbing leg finally nags her awake. The moment her eyes open, invented daytime projects jumble wildly in her head, making her tired before the day begins. And time, racing against her heartbeat, is running out just when she needs more and more of it for everything. Poor heart, it pounds like thunder, trying to respond, and Poochie thinks it's meant for him, that agitated rhythm of her body. He presses his nose into the folds of her neck, breathing little puffs of comfort against her skin. Scratching him behind the ear, she dares at last to remember: tomorrow she'll be eighty.

Yes, she invited them all to her party: Sal, and what's–his–name, Sal's husband. Is it Will? No, that's her son. And Jock, her other son, the youngest one. And they have wives and children too—four altogether she believes: Sarah, Anne.... Oh well, what's in a name? She knows there are ten, eleven counting herself, twelve counting Billy.

"But Billy's been dead for seven years you fool," she whimpers into Poochie's fur, helpless against a sudden barrage of memory—dear sweet funny man, dancing to his death. "Hell, what's life without dancing, old girl? Augh, aging is a bummer," he'd say, doing a soft shoe routine in his patent leather dancing pumps. The bed seems huge without his body, though years before he died they gave up the ritual of sex, not thinking of this as one of many steps toward dying.

Now Poochie shares her bed, and down the hall she has a sewing room, a writing room, a room for guests who never come because she doesn't ask them. The basement is haunted with Halloween ghosts, the smell of damp clay in crocks, and rows and rows of children's art—frogs and pigs and bowls of fruit glazed orange, purple, green.

How had the energy felt, pulsing through her body, on and on through the years of noise and children, cats and guinea pigs and the big police dog Sam who thought he was human? When she asks Sal what energy feels like, Sal looks blank for she's still on the treadmill, assuming that's "life." Poor Sal, will she understand when she has time to think, too much time as time runs out?

Come on, old girl, get going, out into the day where people smile and talk aloud. At last she's up, and Poochie, beside himself with hope, leaps to the floor. "Not yet, Poochie dear," she says as she must each morning. Flinging the window open, she breathes big gulps of summer fog. Way below the garden looks damp, the hollyhocks washed clean. But weeds crowd out the daisies so she turns away and opens the closet door. Reaching through the crush of fabrics for her plaid wool dress, she burrows into old fur and feathers, oranges and pinks—no subtle hues for this old girl. Her house is full of Chinese red, peacock blue, apple green against white walls—a gallery for color. That's why she'll never leave this house.

She puts on a padded bra to hide the hollow of mastectomy, and winds an ace bandage around her stupid leg. Oh well, it walks, poor limb, though at the time, pinned against the garage door, she cried, not from the searing pain, but because she thought she'd lost the battle. Only when she saw their eyes ask "who will keep her?" did she realize that she'd won. So now she must not fall, or forget the flame beneath the empty kettle, or dream as she navigates her old Studebaker down the street avoiding children. For they must never take her from this house.

Hurry, hurry, to the bathroom, down the stairs, careful not to slip. The banister gleams from years of children sliding, always rushing, daring her to scold. And she had scolded, out of fear for their lives, their futures. But now she only recalls their fat bottoms, not the sensation of anger. Cautiously she walks down the stairs, gripping the polished oak, and opens the front door.

Poochie hops over the boxwood hedge and lifts his leg beside the bird bath. She stoops to pick up the morning paper from the brick path, the path she'd laid herself—intricate curving scrolls that defied the rectangular shape of brick. For hours she'd knelt, smoothing the bed of sand, then pressing the bricks into patterns, really playing, but pretending to the others it was work—after all, a path to keep mud carried by little boys' boots and damp dog paws out of the house.

She'd knelt in the flower bed too, painting with plants—shaping, coloring, rearranging nature to suit her whim. These days when she weeds around the primroses she sits on a little Mexican chair, a child's chair. It seems to take forever to accomplish things—projects she's invented to keep from asking what it's all about, this life she clings to with the last remnants of her strength.

But still the voices in her head talk all day long. Sometimes she says "shut up" right out loud, or walks around the block with Poochie so she can talk to puttering neighbors or children on their way to school. The children know she's not crazy, only old, living just outside the rushing life of grown–up people, more like a child herself. That's why they understand.

Creature of habit, she fixes breakfast—half a grapefruit, piece of whole wheat toast, cup of English breakfast tea. She loves to eat, it fills the time. She turns on the oven to heat the kitchen, and knowing she'll forget to turn it off, sets the timer. Now she gives Poochie his dog biscuits because he too is a creature of habit, more so than she, because he has a smaller brain perhaps, though her memory gets fuzzier all the time. Perhaps some day she won't remember that she is going to forget the oven. But she mustn't let that happen or they'll surely make her leave this house; although what's so terrible about leaving the oven on after all? Gas bills, she supposes, but better than spending money on an old folk's home, for she'll never live with the children. The very idea makes her cross, and she quickly spreads out the newspaper on the oilcloth to share in other people's worries.

Reading the Ann Landers column and watching soap operas are only habits now, but when they left home—Sal first, then Will and finally Jock—she and Billy, crazy with freedom and relief that they had finally raised the children, indulged themselves in wasting time. The buzzing timer prods her mind and eyes to focus on the crossword puzzle, but she's a hopeless failure without Billy's help. She places the newspaper on top of a heap of other papers put aside to read later, to try the crossword puzzle later. Riffling through yesterday's mail, mostly junk, she's overwhelmed by the decisions it demands, so she stuffs it into the Chinese basket on top of stacks of other unsolicited requests, furious at the waste of paper.

What is the timer telling her she wonders, looking up at the clock? It's black and green, Art Deco vintage of the 1920's when this house was built, all alone in a field of California poppies, before the crash, when Billy was a carefree rich young man. Later he sold corsets, encyclopedias, anything to keep this house. Eventually a sprinkling of houses, then a crowd, all opened westward to the Bay where ferry boats crossed to San Francisco. Now bridges are strung with vapor lamps that hum all night. But she remembers the old night sounds—wailing trains, and fraternity boys howling like springtime wolves.

Stuck in memories, she stares at the clock. But Poochie claws her knee, and she looks down into his eager button eyes, tears rush into her own—life has always been dreams interrupted by, made real by obligations—dogs to walk, children to feed, birthday parties. And suddenly her mind is clear as she remembers the blackberry patch that she and Poochie discovered in the park, hidden from the path so no one else will find it. She will make a blackberry pie for her birthday and then they'll know she loves them.

From the hall closet where their little jackets used to hang she pulls an old fur coat, a scarf, a knit cap, and wraps herself against her age. Mittens too. And Poochie's leash. A cane to ward off vicious dogs. Oh dear, she needs a bucket for the berries. She goes back to the kitchen and as she pushes open the swinging door a blast of heat engulfs her. She turns off the oven, then carefully lowers herself to her knees and peers under the sink. There, way behind the looping pipe, beyond the plunger and the floor wax, she sees a plastic bucket stuffed with rags—striped shorts of Billy's, a diaper, a sock. And what is this ant poison doing here? Nothing wrong with ants—innocent little insects, not spreading germs like flies or rats. Poochie nips at her heels while she examines rusting cans of cleaning products from long ago when suds and foam meant health.

The yellow linoleum under her knees is spongy, ominous–looking under the breakfast nook where decades of spilled food has not been properly scrubbed because she's always been a slap–dash housekeeper and she has never had more than occasional help—sullen Negro women who take pleasure, just as she does, in ignoring dark corners. Now Negroes are called black. She likes black as a color, the edging of black tile around the sink, setting off the yellow she and Billy chose for the kitchen—"fried eggs sunnyside up," he said, little realizing that eggs would help to kill him in the end. Who knew about cholesterol or ozone layers in those days?

Too bad the bucket's plastic which she knows takes an inordinate amount of energy to produce. Still, as long as it's here, better to use it for something—collecting drippings from a leaky pipe, collecting blackberries—because it can never be disposed of and plastic will litter the nooks and crannies of this earth until eternity. She wonders where she has misplaced the petition against nuclear power plants. But Poochie's nipping optimistically at the heels of her shoes. The crepe soles catch on carpets, and the wedged arches set her off balance. She prefers sneakers, but Sal, having always been a stubborn girl, simply set her jaw and marched her mother into a Red Cross shoe store.

"All right, Poochie, I'm coming, dear," she says, backing out with the bucket and standing up. Staring at the dirty dishes, she clutches the edge of the drainboard. She'll wash them later, after the faintness, for she must not fall and crack her head against the sink. First priority is blackberry picking, then letters to the editor, then dishes if there's any time.

Outside her door the gladioli bloom. The fog hangs thick, but she's comfy in her fur coat, feeling fine with her leg bound up, her cane in hand for extra security. Poochie darts ahead to sniff an approaching Labrador. They are friends; no danger from the Lab and his master, an aging homosexual professor. She starts a conversation about the weather for she's forgotten what his subject is, but he rarely risks a smile, and the two dogs, having finished their communication, rush off in opposite directions. A pair of legs encased in greasy denim stick out from beneath an old

Mercedes–Benz. Carefully she steps across a scattering of tools while Poochie scoots under the car to lick the young man's ear.

"Hey, Poochie, how're ya, fella? Morning, Ma'am," a muffled voice floats out to greet her.

"Good morning, John. We're on our way to the park."

"Far–out. Have a nice day, now."

And that's that, for Poochie scampers down the street, leaving her alone to pass the cracked facades. Too soon the neighborhood has aged. Porch furniture once stretched across with canvas primary color sags in dark corners now. Cobwebs and weeds encroach into the gardens of her mind.

"Poochie," she calls urgently, "where have all the children gone?"

As if in answer, he runs back, circles around her, urges her through the gap in the hedge and down the wooded lane. Light as a whisper, she moves along the path of fallen leaves, following Poochie into a forest she has never really seen before. An animal tracking, she looks for signs in the grey–green leaf patterns strewn on the ground; sniffs the mixed essence of bay, eucalyptus, musty oak; singles out the scent of water. Yes, near the creek is where the berries grow.

"Poochie dear, I do believe this is an adventure," she says as he leads her to the secret opening where the yellow broom parts to let them past. And here the creek splashes on the rocks below. Just off the path, but hidden from it, a tangled thicket of vines hangs heavy with berries inches from her eyes, begging her to pluck them. She pops the first one into her mouth; a cluster of sweetness, it dribbles red juice down her chin and onto her clothes, adding stains of color to all those other stains and colors. Picking the berries fast now, she drops some into the bucket, but eats as many as she collects, pushing deeper into the vines that twist and extend their arms to entwine her as Poochie tugs at her shoelace. She is ageless and wise and joyous, full of that energy she's been trying to remember for years. Yes, this is the way it felt—her heart pounding with anticipation as she stretches her arm through the thorny thicket that tears at her skin, reaching for the biggest berry of them all hanging out there just beyond her grasp.

The creek bank slumps away beneath her Red Cross shoes, tilting her into a hammock of vines, and there she will rest, suspended in the magic berry patch, deaf to Poochie's yip... yip... yip....

Maxine Zalkin

Jewish Brother

Some day I'd like to write a book about
what a Jewish mother
never taught her Jewish son
which is why he grew up
to write a book on
"How to be a Jewish Mother"
instead of "How to be a Jewish Son
Brother to a Jewish Princess"

How come he knows so much
about being a Jewish mother
and not that much about being
a Jewish son but then what do I know
about being a son
since I'm a Jewish mother

Maxine Zalkin

Continuing Education

In Zoology lab
they taught you about planaria
funny looking arrow shaped cross eyed worm
You saw a picture
and maybe even one under a microscope
I'm not sure

then 10 years later they said
they taught some planaria a trick
and then they ground up these planaria and
fed them to those planaria
who didn't know the trick
and those planaria
could do the trick too
though they hadn't been taught

and then a few years later
someone said
that experiment
had been wrong all the time

but 29 years later
as I sat by a river
and looked closely into
small side pools

I saw
wonder of wonderful
real living planaria
with my unexpecting eye

I hadn't known
they were out there
really

Maxine Zalkin

Six Billion People
or Numb Comes from Number

Somewhere
In a philosophy class
She had glimpsed the incredibly complicated problem of
getting from one to two

Somehow
If you could get to two from one
you had taken such a giant step
that the task of getting from two to three and from three
to four and from four to five
was dwarfed

She had been a person
who could never say
one and one is two
She had always said one and one is one and one
And if there were more ones
then there was one and one and one and one
She could never
put people into groups
They were always one and one and one and one to her
And groups of children were always one and one and one

Somehow
it always ended chaotically
because
unless you could put people
and especially children
into groups
however could you relate to them all one to one
It was always her one to their one
and one and one and one and one

Maxine Zalkin

I shop wrong

Inside my home
Inside my head
I decide
what I want
exactly
color
shade and texture
and then
I come looking for it
in this store
and that

A store ought
to have
what I want
I shouldn't have to want
what is
should I

Maxine Zalkin

Liable

If everyone's going this way
and you go that way
you're liable to bump
you're liable to go umph
right up against someone

If you go that way
when everyone's going this way
You're liable

Maxine Zalkin

My Will

I have a plan
to live to be a hundred or more
and in my plan
discovered when another died
and left behind some few belongings
and some file drawers
full of papers
and a question
Who
Who should spend her present with these things
looking through, sorting, discarding
who
(Who is not usually a member of the historical society)

So in my plan
I shall be the who
the one to discard
first the toilet paper rolls
(I thought I might use them for something)
the toys from my children's childhood
the salad bowl someone gave me that I never used
I've already thrown out my education
all those notes
but the letters will have to go

It took fifty years to collect all this stuff
the next fifty are for carefully discarding
so that
it is my plan
I come to the last day
with myself intact
my cot
and one thin blanket

Maxine Zalkin

I saw the bomb

It looked clean
clean cut
white
sparkling white
freshly painted
It looked like maybe a bakery machine
sterile
clean and white

And the oil paintings on the wall
glorious rockets red glare
going here
going there
glorious
glorious oil paintings
there
on the wall as they work on the bomb

Maxine Zalkin

Give all your goods to the poor

You know why don't you
each new thing you bring in takes polish
takes spot remover, ammonia, Ajax, Mr. Clean Oxydol
Woolite
each new thing you bring in takes work
and time
give all your goods to the poor
subtract don't add
Let the poor have all your troubles

Maxine Zalkin

Shoes

I broke my toe
the little toe
on my left foot
I stubbed it too furiously
so that the pain could get out here
out of hiding
and I could yowl
legitimately
moan
and they could accept my groans
because it was so obvious
I was in pain
see
how swollen and red

But no
That's another poem

This one is about the shoes I had to wear
to accommodate the swelling
my son's huge running shoes
two tone blue
and as I walked around town
a girl in a group of teen agers
stared at them
and even though
I caught her eye in half challenge
half warning
I heard her say
as we passed
did you see her shoes

Maxine Zalkin

Wild Ride

No wonder I've been having trouble keeping my balance
I just found out
I mean I probably read it before or heard it before
but I just now really found out
I mean it clicked in there
really connected this time around
that this round globe I'm standing on
(and I've pretty much grown up with the idea that it is
round
although it seems pretty flat where I'm standing)
that this round globe
(not a globe really you understand
that's just what we represent it as
inside our geography classes
and inside our studies like in House Beautiful
or in what everybody knows is a proper English upper
class study
or the study of some deacon for that matter
where they always have these fancy globes balanced on
stands)
this huge bumpy ball of molten rock solidified on the
outside like a crust of bread
french bread
(there are French people on it with me
although I hadn't exactly realized they were with me)
we're all going
(the French people and me)
we're all going round at a rate so fast
only the people in the Concord would realize
(and even inside there I'll bet they don't
not with all that music and those stewards)

We're going around so fast it's all we can do to simply
hang on
we're going
(are you ready for this)
we're taking a spin 1,000 miles an hour
all the time
even while we're sleeping
and that spin is stirring up a good old wind
that spin is sloshing our oceans right up against our land

I didn't used to be so vulnerable living back there in the
middle of the continent
but now
but now I live right here in the really dangerous part

while the earth is spinning madly
it says
it tends to spin right out from under the oceans and leave
them behind
and since the spin is eastward
(that's why the Moslems face east when they pray
I would too
if I had realized all this)
since the spin is eastward
the waters tend to pile up along western shores that's
where I am
and the waters in the middle of the seas
are sloshing and whirling in great whirlpools
and rivers
and everything's moving at a mad pace
and the winds

and then the tides
the sun
and the moon are pulling at us
the winds are only roiling up the surface of things
but the tides
the tides are moving the whole ocean
and for that matter
they are pulling the earth and the air too
every time there is a ten foot tide in the water it says
the continents rise about six inches
(have you been feeling like you're being pulled apart lately)
and nobody can tell me
that if the moon can pull up on a whole sea
it can't pull up on me
and there's no place to run
no place on this earth of ours
there's no place at all
unless maybe you got into a space shuttle

I heard we were made of a rather large percentage of
water ourselves
so I'm quite sure we have little tidal waves all over the
place under our own skin even

no wonder I've been having trouble
keeping my equilibrium

Maxine Zalkin

Cat

cat
fat bellied cat
it's a fact
that
you are going to have kittens
maybe you didn't expect this
when you were lying in the sun
smiling and smiling at
that other cat
(that cat that was not female)
maybe you don't know that you're expecting
but now
it's too late to know
that this
has anything to do with that

Maxine Zalkin

Rubber bands

Have you noticed
Do you know about them
I didn't
I didn't know
a paper boy has to pay for his own
I didn't know one day's throw away ad could use up my
entire can
of Saved rubber bands
I never noticed that you can find rubber bands
everywhere
on sidewalks and streets
that if you go for a long walk
picking up rubber bands
as a kind of bending over exercise
you can come home
with a whole pocketful
did you know rubber bands
disintegrate in the sun
that if you try to wind an old one around a rolled up
paper
it snaps apart easily
if it's one of those
that has been lying around a while
But I know now
When I see a little
plastic bag of rubber bands on someone's dashboard
I smile with the knowledge
a paper boy's mother is driving that van

Maxine Zalkin

Alarm

What a way to wake up shake up
with a ridiculously high peeping sound
shrieking all the way through sleep
shriek awake
time!
It is time
get up
It's time to get up in the morning
tiny mechanism
invented on purpose to disturb–interrupt
morning's sleeping thoughts
it is day
it is time
warmth and comforters and
the shriek awakes
with the mechanics of an outer timing
what a way to wake up life
from the dead of night

p.s.
added my husband
who has the tiny wristwatch shrieker
but that's what got you going
on these three poems

Maxine Zalkin

Far Out

I went far far far out
to go into the wilderness
where the wild man was
who came out wild and raging
and axed the campers
and nobody stopped him
until three lay dead
nobody stopped him although there
were many many more of them
than he was
 I went far far out
miles out
along a dusty bumpy roadway
which had a fence alongside it
and explosions and
warnings of explosions
and testings came from inside that
fenced out wilderness printed and posted all along that
fenced in wilderness
 I went far far
and far and far
to the end of the land of wild honey
and locusts
the fasting for 40 days wilderness
and I found in going into the wilderness
that you must bring out the emptys
crushed slightly by your own hand
the 7 up cans you took in with you cool and full

Jane Strong

The Rescue

The sharp peal of the telephone startled her. It rescued her from that revolting thing, but in her rush to get out of the kitchen, she bumped her shoulder on the door jamb. The phone rang again. I'm coming, I'm coming, don't go away. She ran into the room, snatched the instrument before it could escape, carried it over with its long tail dragging to her tawny plush chair, flopped down into it, and lifted the phone just as its jaws opened to roar again.

"Hel–lo?" Her voice was breathy into the mouthpiece.

"Hello," he said.

"Oh, Alan," she said, rubbing the place where the door had hit her, "I was just about to call you. I have a favor to ask…?"

"A favor? How nice!" The voice was so warm and friendly that she wanted to curl up in the big chair with it. But something about it was not Alan, Alan who lived on the third floor and was married to Margaret. No, not Alan at all.

"This isn't Alan. Who is this?"

"I didn't say it was Alan." The voice paused. "I'm sorry. If that's who you wanted me to be, I'd almost wish I were Alan. For you." The voice sounded genuinely sorry. Yet, at the same time there was intelligence, amusement, a glint of humor? Was he in some way making fun of her?

"Not at all," she said stiffly. "That is, I was expecting—I was just thinking about calling Alan. And then when you called…" Lenore wondered why she bothered to explain. Why didn't she just hang up. Obviously, it was a wrong number. Wasn't it?

"I understand." Really it seemed as if he did understand. There was a calm gentle quality to the man's voice. How much you could sometimes feel of the person there in the voice, if it were a richly human one like this. For a moment she wished she did indeed know this person, but she knew with a certainty that she did not. It was not Alan, or the man who tried to sell her life insurance, not Dr. Digman, no one she worked with, not anyone she knew. Nor any voice she had ever heard before. She squirmed around in the deep chair, placed both feet on the floor, and sat up straight.

"Who did you wish to speak to?" she asked in crisp tones.

"Ahhh." He sighed. "I've offended you. My apology."

"I'm afraid I don't know you," Lenore said, frostily. "I'm afraid you have the wrong number." Like a stupid broken record saying, I'm afraid. She found herself trembling with cold, her teeth fairly chattering. She extended the receiver toward the stand. In a moment it would be cradled and the connection would be broken, but she found herself bending toward the telephone as if there were some message that still might come through to her after all.

"Wait! Don't hang up!" As if he could see what she was about to do.

"Well?" She wouldn't be trifled with.

"You're quite right to be annoyed with me," said the voice in a cheerful but confident matter–of–fact manner. "I was calling someone else and I dialed the wrong number, but"—here the voice slipped into a new persuasive tone, "—but then I got you." Immediately the voice was warmer, friendlier.

Lenore could almost see the personage behind the voice as belonging to the sort of man who, she imagined, when he came home from work (in his conventional dark suit), would change into a silky dressing gown. She pictured him wearing it now, dark in tones of maroon and black with threads of gold, the shawl collar of maroon satin, a cord of dark silk looped around his waist. A smoking jacket, perhaps, she thought, her imaginary picture of his face obscured as if by smoke.

"It was chance that brought us together," he said, "but now I can't let you go. Your voice has put sunshine into my day. Unexpectedly, a day that started out to be very ordinary has become—" (He hesitated, as if afraid of saying too much.) "—something quite extraordinary. Do you mind? How often does that happen?"

"Well, I don't know, but I'm afraid—" That word again.

"Don't be afraid." The voice gently coiled in her ear. "How can it do any harm for us to talk a little?"

"I'm sorry." She could see herself being stiff and unbending and conventional. Maybe other women could be more relaxed. "I don't know who you are, and I'm not accustomed..."

"Of course, you're not!" the voice interposed swiftly. "Let me introduce myself. My name is Adrian," he said formally. But then immediately he added in a confidential tone, friend to friend. "Odd name, eh? Does it seem strange to you? My grandfather's name. He was half–Italian, half–English, a sea–captain. A romantic figure to me as a boy, as you can imagine."

She murmured assent.

"But now it's only fair, since your beautiful voice has lifted my spirit, that you tell me your name. Just your first name, please."

"It's Lenore," she said politely, and was immediately horrified at what she had done. "I can't talk to you," she said in a panic. "I don't know you. You have no right to talk to me. You're a complete stranger. Good bye!" She hung up.

Why had she given him her name? If only she could call the words back but now it was too late. Almost in tears but not quite crying, she murmured the words go away, go away, to the empty room until the words lost their meaning. Then, drawing her breath in a soft moan, she sighed and was quiet.

The silence of the room pressed around her and she became aware that she had buried her face in her hands. She was being foolish, as her mother used to say. There was no one here.

There was no sound in her apartment, or the apartment next door, or anywhere in the building. No sounds of feet walking, of clattering rubbish cans, of the elevator, of the incinerator. No noises of Sunday morning shoppers slamming their car doors from the parking lot of the food market across the way. No grocery carts clattering over rough pavement, no parents calling their kids. No noises whatsoever except the distant roar of traffic somewhere far away—unless it was the low drumming sound of her own heart?—which one could almost imagine to be the sea.

The phone rang. Slowly she reached for it but held her hand in midair until the phone rang again. She could feel the sound resonating through her whole body and trembled in response to it. On the third ring, she picked up the telephone.

"Hello?" She made her voice casual and easy, as if she might be expecting any one of a dozen people. "Oh. It's you."

"Yes, it's me, Adrian. Of course, it's me. How do you think I feel you hanging up on me like that? Please don't ever do that to me again. Lenore?"

"Yes. What?" She looked at the black phone as if there might be some sign on the device by which she could tell what she needed to know. She waited.

"Lenore, listen to me. Suppose we met through friends, or at church—do you go to church?—or at the supermarket?" He knew about the market? "We might have met at an art gallery, or been in the same night school class. These days people find each other in unusual ways...Lenore, isn't that right?"

"I suppose. Yes."

"Well then, you see? A friend doesn't hang up on a friend." That much was true.

"Dear Lenore, please don't go away from me. Do you believe in Chance? We could be destined to meet each other... Do you know you have a beautiful voice, Lenore. Do many people say that to you?" No, no one ever had. "I think you can tell a lot about a person from their voice. Don't you?" His own voice was calm and quiet. She wondered how old he was. He was asking her a question.

"What?"

"Would you tell me something honestly?"

"What?"

"Do you think Adrian is a strange name?"

In her mind, a dark attic filled with junk, a flashlight suddenly focused its narrow beam on a single thing: Adrian.

"Wasn't there some painter designer in Hollywood? Married to the old time movie actress Janet Gaynor?" Surprised, she heard her voice chatting away as if to an old friend.

"Exactly! Oh Lenore, I love you for saying that! You're a very clever woman. Most people just stare blankly and say, 'Adrian? That's an odd name'."

He was right. Her own name had not always been easy.

"Lenore." He said the name gently. "That's a lovely name. It makes me think of sadness and beauty. Why sadness? Poe, I suppose: The Lady Lenore?"

Sometimes he sounded like an older man, cultured, well–read, maybe even well–to–do. But other times he sounded younger.

"What are you thinking?" She felt herself blush. But fortunately he went right on. "Do you know how I picture you? Dark hair, fair skin but dark eyes, deep set, dark brown almost black—. Am I close?"

It was hardly a question. It was almost as if he knew. As if one of those inventions of the future you read about had made it possible for him to see the person he was talking to. Or could he be watching her with binoculars from some apartment building? She glanced wildly around the room.

"Lenore? Don't go away. You're not a blonde, are you? Say you're not a blonde!"

"I'm not a blonde," she said, and giggled. Before she could recover and pull back from it, he had swooped in and pounced on her giggle as if it were an admission. As if in some game between them, her position had lost ground and his had advanced.

His voice was full of laughter. "Thank you for not being a blonde. Blondes are boring, don't you think?"

No one had ever said that! 'Blondes have more fun.' Or, 'Gentlemen prefer blondes.' People said those things. Boring! She smiled.

"Lenore."

"Yes?"

"It's really a Greek name, Lenore, isn't it? Meaning Light. A beautiful name. Light in a dark world. What could be better?"

What was he doing, sitting there with a name book on his lap reading off the meanings? No one had ever paid that much attention to her name before.

"How do you know so much about names?"

"It's my hobby. One of them." His voice took on a soft but compelling tone. "I feel you can tell a lot about a person by his name. Your name affects your life—do you believe that? The name 'Adrian' has certainly affected my life." His voice had the timbre almost of an actor. It made her shiver. "And the name 'Lenore' has a rich dark effect..."

Lenore fingered her hair and her mouth came open.

"But Alan. What about Alan?" Adrian's voice had turned remote and cool.

"Alan?" She had forgotten all about Alan.

"Is he your boyfriend, this Alan? Your man?"

Alan, how did he know about Alan, Lenore wondered. Suddenly she stiffened in the chair, her back rigid, her knuckles gripping the receiver as she remembered the horrible thing! The dead creature in the trap under her sink. "Oh God, no!"

"What's the matter? What happened?" Adrian's voice swept to her rescue like a wave rushing up a beach. "What is it? Does it have to do with Alan?"

"No, no. Well, this awful thing...Ohh!" She shuddered.

"Tell me."

"Well, that is, Alan's a friend of mine and I wanted him to help me with—Well, this horrible thing happened—but maybe you wouldn't think it's anything at all...? You'd say I was a fool..." She was chewing her lip in agitation, and now there was a sore place, an exposed spot of new baby skin where she had bitten off a fleck of old dry skin. Part of her wanted to go look in the mirror to see if it were bright red, perhaps even bleeding...?

"Lenore, go slowly. Just tell me what's the matter. Maybe I can help you."

"You see it's this horrid rat, mouse, I guess. I mean, it's nothing. I just caught it in a trap under the kitchen sink. And I—I just can't bear to think about it."

His voice was sympathetic. "You mean you had to take it out of the trap?"

"No, no, it's still there!" she wailed. What was she doing explaining about the mouse to a perfect stranger? But he had grasped the situation.

"Of course. You want somebody to get rid of the mouse for you, right? That's it, isn't it?"

"Yes," she breathed gratefully. "That's it. I can't stand the thought of touching it. I was going to ask Alan—""

But you didn't—?"

"No, because it's too early, and—"

"Good! Maybe Alan's not good at that, Alan's squeamish—"

Actually, she thought, Alan *was* a bit squeamish.

"But I understand these things," Adrian said with smooth confidence. "I understand perfectly why you feel that way, because I'm phobic about snakes. It's quite irrational and unscientific, I know that, but still... For you, it's mice, right?"

"Oh yes, yes. The very idea of them—"

"I know exactly what you mean! Not to worry. I'll get rid of it for you. No problem."

"I wish you would," said Lenore. "I mean, I wish you could." She giggled again, that brief momentary giggle. It was such a relief. Immediately she realized that she was talking to this stranger as if he were her friend. What would her mother think? Or anyone? Was it unwise, was it dangerous, was it—what? For a moment, she was at sea. She stared at the telephone as if she'd never seen one before.

"Lenore? Come back!" The voice curled up out of the phone in agitation, and she almost smiled to hear it as if she were rather pleased at the thought of an agitated man. She lifted the receiver back toward her ear, yet held it away from her flesh an inch, teasing, so it would not touch the ear yet, but close, close, so that she could hear Adrian's voice.

"Come back, I've lost you." The voice folded about her like silk. "Lenore, I know what you're thinking. You're thinking you don't know this man, Adrian, and how can he help you? Right?"

Exactly! Lenore, holding the phone near her ear, nodded and said nothing.

"Right," continued Adrian, satisfied. "But a moment ago we were friends. It's true, isn't it? Admit it."

"Yes." Her voice was almost inaudible. She stared down at her blouse as if the faint movement of the white material would reveal to herself her true feelings.

She had indeed begun to regard him as a friend. But this was all wrong, wasn't it? It was wicked, dangerous, tempting. We live in a world of unknown possibilities, good and bad, of fearful danger, accidents, threats, violence, yes, but also of other possibilities, luck, friendship, happiness, love—? Who knew what lay just beyond the old familiar routines, down the next street, in the heart of the next—what? She'd lost the thought.

Two people inside her fought over the telephone; one, urged her to hang up and end this before some terrible point of no return; but the other one wanted to wait, to go on listening, talking to Adrian, following wherever it led. She leaned forward, half out of her chair, gripping the receiver in both hands, her knuckles white with effort, trying to hang up.

"We were becoming good friends there, for a while. But now, something's changed. You're worried. Am I right?"

"Yes," she said honestly. "I don't know you. It's crazy for me to listen to you. You're a stranger. I should hang up. I'm going to hang up." She was tense in her chair, torn between what she knew she should do and her reluctance to do it.

"Dear Lenore." He was actually laughing! "But of course you feel that way. It's only natural, does you credit. Look on it as if we had just met—at a boring cocktail party—stranger one moment, acquaintance, maybe friend, the next. You know how it goes...Hold it, Lenore, there's someone at my door."

Lenore opened her mouth to speak.

"I'll call you back." he said, and hung up.

He hung up.

Lenore came to her feet, gripped the chair, laid her hand over her heart. She couldn't feel a thing. Her mouth was open and she was gasping for strength like a fish thrown on land. Straining, listening, concentrating. As if she had been wakened abruptly by some concussion which she had not heard but only felt its effect. Now she was waiting for the aftershock so she could orient herself to the situation, whatever it was. She listened intently to the silence—had it ever been so quiet on a Sunday morning?

Once, still in school, Mother away for the weekend, she had been typing late on someone's term paper to earn some money, and had fallen asleep on the daybed. When she awoke the apartment was rumbling as if a large truck was going by. Dishes trembled in the kitchen and typed pages fanned soundlessly across the card table and onto the floor. Silence.

Still tangled in a dream, she had been too sleepy to investigate and fell immediately back into a heavy sleep from which she remembered nothing. In the morning, she saw the pages on the rug. Later she learned there had been an earthquake. In the kitchen, when she went to investigate, everything seemed as usual except for the slim curved handle of one coffee cup from Mother's good set which lay on its saucer, a small cream–colored question mark. She never told her mother and now Mother was dead.

Had she gone to her death believing Lenore broke the handle to her coffee cup? Had she never forgiven her for being afraid to admit it? Suddenly Lenore felt burdened with guilt, as if she had actually broken it, deliberately broken it, and then hidden it from her mother. Lied about it, lied. Something they had in common, a refusal to accept the fact that things got broken, an unwillingness to believe in accidents. Without ever meaning to, from some strange place within themselves, people attracted disaster.

She felt chilled, as if she had been sitting in a draft too long. Shivering, she went into the bedroom to get her sweater, pulling it up over her cold arms with stiff fingers, and even buttoning a few buttons clumsily. The bed stared at her, crumpled and tossed about as if some struggle had taken place. Quickly she bent to straighten up the bed.

She pulled the blanket edge from underneath the spread, jerking out the wrinkles as her mother used to jerk out the wrinkles of her blouse, reaching up under Lenore's skirt with her cold, slightly rough hand to give a sharp tug on the shirt–tail while Lenore stood blushing from a feeling of shame.

Lenore was tucking the bedspread around the pillow when the teakettle squealed. She dropped the spread and ran to the kitchen to snatch the kettle off the burner, which she had no memory of having turned on. In her haste to grab the kettle, she overturned a dish of graham crackers and milk, splashing the rest of the brownish crumb–filled milk onto the counter where it spilled down the cupboard door and dripped onto the floor. She reached under the sink for the big sponge and the bottle of cleaner, thrusting her hand back into the dark recesses of the under–sink area—and let out screams.

Her fingers met that moist furry object, that loathsome feel of the stiff hairs on the smooth rounded flesh and the prickly whiskers, even the face, the eyes, all in a single instant… she would die! Coughing, slamming the door shut with her knee, she turned on the faucet with her other, her uncontaminated hand and began vigorously washing her hands under the running water, soaping, scrubbing, not looking at what it might be that she was washing away…

She dried her poor hands, all red with the washing, took a wedge of lemon she had cut for ice tea, rubbed it all over her fingers, rinsed them a final time in cold water. Taking a second paper towel to dry them, she crumpled it and threw it after the first into the kitchen wastebasket which stood in the corner of the room. (Thank God it wasn't under the sink!) Slowly she brought her hand toward her face and sniffed the scrubbed, chapped fingers. The faintest fragrance of lemon, that was all. She was glad no one had heard her screaming, or if they had, they had paid no attention. Too bad about the graham crackers, she thought, although they would have been soggy by now in any case.

When the phone rang, she ran to it, pulse racing, mind carefully empty. She waited for a moment, picked up the telephone, held the receiver to her ear, and spoke hesitantly into the mouthpiece:

"Hello?" Her voice rasped in her ears, as if it had not been used for a long time.

"Lenore?"

"Yes."

"It's Adrian. Finally got rid of my visitor and I'm on my way over to deal with the beast."

Lenore shuddered and made a small sound of revulsion. "I just touched it."

"Poor darling! It won't be long now, and then, no more mouse. How's the fastest way to get there, coming from downtown. Out Fifth?"

She explained the best way to come out, gave him the address and told him he could park in the parking lot of the nearby market.

"Be of good cheer. Your torment will soon be over. I should be there in less than fifteen minutes," he promised.

It was not until after she hung up and was combing her hair that it came to her that she had actually given him her address.

Oh, God. What had she done? What in the world was she thinking about? Inviting a total stranger to her apartment, someone she had never seen, someone she had only talked to by telephone, not even a friend of a friend or anything.

What would her mother have said if she had been alive? There are some things you do and some things you don't do, that's all. You try to live your life between the two. A girl that invites a man to her apartment invites trouble. Or was it a girl who goes to a man's apartment is "just asking for it"? That was one of her mother's favorite expressions. What sort of terrible things did her mother think happened in apartments between a woman and a man? Were apartments more risky than houses? Had certain things happened to her own mother that she never spoke of? What a strange idea!

Lenore jumped up, ran into the bathroom, stripped off her clothes, filled the washbasin and began soaping herself. A sponge bath..."a lady always keeps herself clean...", so sad somehow, sponge baths in rooming houses, basins of water, sponging... fragmentary images of her mother...

What was she doing? She stared at herself in the mirror trying to determine whether or not she was clean. She was clean, of course she was clean, she'd had a shower. So it was more, did she look clean? Never mind, she told herself, never mind. What difference does it make if you're clean, you'll soon be dirty.... What did that mean?

That was another thing of her mother's. "No sooner do I get you all cleaned up but you get dirty again." Something like that. Well, if her mother was going to be here with them every minute that would certainly cramp her style. She would get nowhere that way. She had a sudden picture of the three of them on the bed making polite conversation, while her mother tried to find out what Adrian did, what his prospects were, how much money he made. Her mother would ask about his family, if she knew any of his people.

Lenore giggled and rubbed her eyebrow with a wet finger. More lipstick. Blot it off again. Her hair. She arranged it over and over, in a new way, down over her face more, bangs, brushed back, working very rapidly, feverishly now. Good Lord, time was passing. He'd be here any minute. There! That was a little different, but basically the same. Easy to tidy again if it were messed up...Thoughts scudded across the floor of her mind like dry leaves in a wind; she had no say in the matter. But all the excitement had put color in her cheeks, and she really looked—eyes sparkling, the flush beneath the skin—not too bad. She was pleased. She held up a mirror and looked at the back of her head. Yes.

What was that! She lowered the mirror without a sound and froze, listening intently. Footsteps. Someone was walking along the outside corridor. *How could he be here so soon?* Grabbing a bath towel, she rubbed herself all over, threw the towel in the direction of the hamper, ran into the bedroom, hurried into her panties and bra, and was frantically trying to fasten the hooks on her bra, when she realized the footsteps had stopped. She had a little time. He wasn't here yet. A fine mist of perspiration which lay on the surface of her flesh felt cooler now; the breath of relief came like a faint breeze across her skin.

She slipped on a white peasant blouse, and considered the next step. Pants were safer but a skirt was more becoming to her figure, she thought, and selected her navy skirt, circular cut with bands of bright weaving around the bottom, actually a folk dance skirt... Perhaps she could go to Yugoslavia or Greece?... Maybe if she went to Israel it would still not be too late. She could join a *kibbutz* or something. Did they let non–Jews do that?

Dressed, she looked at herself in the long mirror, twirling the skirt in some opening, closing movements like a flower opening to be—whatever they call it, pollinated, and closing again on the pollen—was that what happened? Some slow motion Disney–type movie of the life cycle of a flower, was that where she'd seen it?

What time was it? Her watch seemed to have stopped. This old fashioned windup gold wristwatch inherited from her mother had a way of coming to a stop without warning. Quickly she tiptoed to the closed blinds which gave on the outside corridor and peered between the slats. No one. Good, it was too early yet anyway. She set the watch by the clock beside the TV. Maybe his estimate was off about the fifteen minutes. He wouldn't have had time to get here from downtown anyway, yet he seemed to know the market she used as a landmark. Now she wished she had gone shopping and had more food in the house. At least she could give him some coffee. But first, music?

She felt jittery and nervous as if she were meeting some test which she hadn't studied for. Follow out the folk dance theme, she told herself. Rapidly she ran through her records, chose six of the best dance records, arranged their holes over the spike of her old-fashioned player and tripped the switch. Greek Dance Party slipped down the shaft and began to play.

Now she hurried to the kitchen to arrange things: a stack of old newspapers on the counter, a large paper sack, tongs, rubber gloves? Ugh! A roll of paper toweling and a bottle of pine oil. Also, an old bottle of Lysol someone had left. Enough.

She stood in front of the sink, her hands resting on the counter, her knee against the closed doors to the cupboard below when somehow her legs started trembling, and the rattling sound of skin-covered bone against wood was so terrifying that for a moment she thought the poor massacred mouse was still alive and was drumming on the wall demanding release from its prison, was dragging the cruel trap and its bloody haunches behind it to the door against which it beat with all its dying force.

A quake of revulsion welled up through the floor boards, up her legs to her pelvis, knotting its contents, rolling hotly up through her belly and rib cage into her chest, bulging in her throat...Her jaw clenched, her lips pulled back in a grimace of agony, her head fell forward and she shuddered a long shudder of almost orgasmic relief...

Ahhhhhh. So, she was not to be sick after all. Luckily. Actually she felt better after it as one is supposed to feel after the vomiting and the nausea recedes. Something was over, some personal earthquake, and like the real earthquake she had once felt, the damage was, apparently, negligible.

Coffee cups. Hers were ceramic mugs from the seconds sale at the pottery shop but very nice. It would surely be an act of kindnness to offer Adrian coffee, after his—gallant act.

("I hope you don't mind instant?"

"No, not at all.")

On the black tole tray with the painted roses, she arranged the fat little jar of Yuban, the sugar bowl, the small container of powdered imitation cream, the two mugs, the Edelweiss spoon, two paper napkins with a design of purple iris and yellow jonquil, and carried it over to the narrow table against the wall. The work of disposal at the sink would need space. Anything else he needed he could ask for when he got here. Whatever it was he wanted, she would certainly try to provide...

Think of it as if she had met him somewhere, introduced by a friend at an art reception, as a volunteer working at the Funeral and Memorial Society, or stuffing envelopes for a political candidate, or collecting for the Red Cross. After you got out of school there was really no place to meet people and get to know them, and society had abandoned the problem.

In cities, particularly, where the anonymnity and the loneliness persisted there was a constant flow of strangers pressing against you. You were in a crowd of people, intimate as lovers, but the faces were blank and turned away.

Sometimes you passed someone on the street, you glanced at him as long as he was not looking at you, and you saw him flick his glance away like a cigarette in the instant before connection. But sometimes the two of you, total strangers, met and connected, for just an instant, looked into each other's eyes with more intimacy and naked openness than you had with friends. Who knew what perilous risks or marvelous luck might rule the world? Destiny, luck, good or bad, what else was there? Like the cheap candy "chances" she squandered her pennies on in gradeschool, hoping one of them would have a cherry in the center, and she could win a prize, a big candy bar, or whatever she wanted to choose.

The ringing of her bell did not surprise her. She knew he would come. There was an inevitability about it which would lead somewhere new. Good or bad, but new. Slowly, with surprising calm, she walked toward the door, toward the bell which rang a second time. I'm coming, she thought, moving toward the rescuer who would release the mouse from its trap, too late for the mouse, already dead, but not perhaps too late for her.

Lenore opened her door. The morning sunshine welled up around the figure in the doorway and poured into her dark room.

Mollie Poupeney

OREGON POEMS

Daddy

He cut a length and
held it in his hands,
gently twisting, then
he eased the sheath of
bark free to carve the
notch and shape the
mouthpiece.

It's so white underneath,
I said. And smooth as a
baby's bottom, he said and
pinched me as he put the
whistle to his lips for
one sweet note. I who
dreamed of becoming a bird
try it now.

It doesn't work, I said.

Gently, he said, and wiped
away my spit.

Whisper your music, he
whispered into my ear.

Mollie Poupeney

Oregon Revisited 1977

He is tallstooped skinny and
pure bald. His legs shake when
he answers the door. We were
neighbors once when I was nine
years old. Now he is eighty.

> "They used to call me Curly.
> Didn't last long— then they
> called me Slats for awhile."

I had driven many days collecting.
My childhood roots had withered early
beneath the Douglas fir.

> "They always give you nicknames in
> the woods. I think about that a lot."

Withered but not dead. What could he tell
me about my father?

> "Your mother made the best baking
> powder biscuits around. She always
> kept you kids clean. Is she still
> living?"

Did he work with my father after 1935?
Did he see him much after the war?
Did he know that my father was dead?

"Your dad and me, we worked a few
jobs. He ran the loading donkey.
Me, I was the donkey doctor. Smokey
was a skookum man."

Did he know my father stopped drinking a few
years before he died, after I was married and
had three babies?

Silence.

Was he friends with my father?

"We drank from the same bottle— "

I must leave, I say good–bye. He calls to me
through the screen door.

"How did he do it?" he calls.

Mollie Poupeney

Mrs. Green

I worked with your dad
at Consolidated Lumber,
she says. We had a big
kitchen, pastry cook,
everything. Served two
hundred men, nine girls.
Sure they cussed a lot
and teased the flunkies,
but they was good men.
Worked hard.

You're fifty?
she says
and slaps my arm. Why,
when you get to be seventy–
five like me no one's
gonna know it. My boy's
forty–three and
he looks like an old man.

Buddy! Come here! I
want you to meet Smokey's
girl!

Mollie Poupeney

Irma

Some of them were grey
silver in the late day
when there was a sun,
veering toward black
in the rain

Not much use to paint
when the salt air turned
around and peeled the
paint in no time, she
said about the houses
they rented
they was just mostly
shacks, she said,
anyhow

Your mother always had
the prettiest curtains

Always sewing something

Mollie Poupeney

Jack Murphy

If someone got killed
on the job they never said
someone got killed, they'd
just say "they killed a man
in the woods today". Maybe
it wasn't where you was
working but you'd hear about
it. Word would come down
the line, maybe from up on
the Saddle, maybe from one
of the sides in your own
outfit, one guy would tell
another.

Well, they'd killed a man
in the woods this day and
Smokey and me got us a gallon
and sat around that
night. We got to talking and
such as that and one thing
led to another and before we
knew what was happening we was
having this fight. Well, your
dad, he was oldern me and I
had always looked up to him, but
that night I knocked him out
cold. I always felt kind of bad
about that.

The whiskey was suppose to
last us the month but we sure
put a dent in it that night.

Mollie Poupeney

Emma

She was always washing
bedsheets and draping them
around the stove. I guess
one of you kids wet the
bed, I don't know, maybe
not. When there was any
sun she would get them out
on the line real early and
she would keep going out all
day feeling them for when
they would be dry.

She always got them in
before dark, before the
tramps could steal them
and sell them down the
line for food.

Lots of time there wouldn't
be no sun.

She always ironed them sheets,
I remember that much.

Mollie Poupeney

Jewel

They used to call you Carrie
Potts when you was little. People
was always giving people nicknames,
and you had to carry the slopjars
from under the bed and empty them
in the outhouse every morning, so
that's what they called you, Carrie
Potts. You hated it, I remember that
much

Later on they called you Mammy Yokum.
We was always calling each other
funny names. You remember when
they used to call you that?

I bet you don't.

Mollie Poupeney

At Newport School

they used to have hot
lunches for a nickel
but if the kid had no
money he could say so and
eat free. Your mama was
too proud to take something
she couldn't pay for, so if
she didn't have no nickel to
give you she made you take
a sandwich to school. You
must've been six or seven and
chewed on the nickel
tied in the corner of a
handkerchief one day. Anyhow,
you swallowed the nickel. You
cried because you wanted the
Jello so the teacher let you
eat, and the next day she made
you sit until you had a BM.
Then she took a ruler and poked
until she got that nickel which
she gave to the cafeteria to
pay for the lunch you had
eaten the day before.

Your daddy called you the
human slot machine and
your mama made you promise
never to chew on handkerchiefs.

Do you remember that?

Mollie Poupeney

Second Cousin

They gave out cod
liver oil at the town
school— it rained all
winter on the coast and
I guess this was supposed
to make you kids healthy.
The teacher called it liquid
sunshine, and it was free.

You brought home a mayonaise
jar full and tried to
give it to your little
brother. Your mother made
you take a spoonful to show
him how good it was, and
you vomited all over the chopping
block in the woodshed.

Your mother laughed until
she cried, your little brother
never did take none.

Mollie Poupeney

Big Brother

Your brother peeled chittum
bark in the spring and sold
it somehow to somebody. Never
did know what the real name
was for that tree, but they
used it to make laxatives, I
know that much.

We just called it chittum.

Mollie Poupeney

Ray

I remember this one time
I came home late with
Smokey. We'd had a few,
and he woke you kids up
and got you out of bed to
sing me some of the old
songs he had taught you.

You refused to sing,
I remember that, but
I never will forget
your big brother standing
there in his underwear
singing for his old man,
tears running down your
daddy's cheeks.

What's your brother doing now?

Mollie Poupeney

Bert

If we wasn't catching steelhead
we was getting us a buck,
bringing it home for the women
to can. You never tasted nothing
til you tasted venison home canned
in a jar.

One winter we got us a bear. The
women was canning for a week.
They canned anything we could
catch, salmon, Dungeness crab,
razor clams.

They say it was hard times but
we always ate good.

One time we stole us some
chickens, but we was drunk
when we did that.

Mollie Poupeney

The bees had all this honey

stuck in the tree and we
figured why let the bears
have it, so your Dad and me
and Wooden Eye, we got all
wrapped up and had torches
and got that honey out of
that tree. We let Wooden
Eye go first since he didn't
have as much to lose.

Your dad was laughing
and singing— bees didn't
scare him none.

Now if it had been a treeful
of snakes—

Mollie Poupeney

Dragsaw Smitty

Your dad told the hook
tender one time to get
rid of this punk choker
setter who was fouling
up the lines or he would
walk off the job.

He figured anybody
working in the woods had
to have a lot of savvy
or somebody could get
himself killed. And
him being on the yarder
donkey, Smokey had to work
with this joe magee.

What he said was, that
man's so goddam dumb he
thinks Christ was run
over by a switch
engine

Mollie Poupeney

The fiddler was blind

but he could play and
his brother played the
saw. God, we danced!
And you kids asleep on
the benches covered with
coats. Any man look at
your mother, he'd have to
deal with Smokey outside
the hall. If a fight broke
out inside the women would
wrap you kids up in the coats
and get ready to leave, unless
the driver was right in the
thick of it. Your dad and me,
we didn't own no car, but it
didn't matter.

We was usually in the thick
of it anyhow.

Mollie Poupeney

Elaine

I used to baby sit you kids
so's your dad and mother could
go to a dance in town

One time we had a pot luck
dinner and your mother worked
all day cooking chicken and
a big potato salad and
everybody came

We ate outside and your dad
and I sat down on one of
those picnic tables with the
benches nailed to the side

Well, nobody sat on the other
side and we just tipped that
whole table onto ourselves and
we was covered with pickles
and olives and potato salad
and fried chicken, what didn't
all land in the dirt

Your dad laughed until he got
tears in his eyes and your
mother cried and went into
the house

I don't know where you kids
was then, but I landed on
the ground with your dad,
I know that much

Mollie Poupeney

She was grownup and married

and had a baby. She had red
hair and wore thick maroon
lipstick and puce lacquered
fingernails.

Mine were stubby–chewed and
dirty under the quick with
one stiff hangnail always bleeding.

It wasn't her temper that made
her throw the coffee pot and
cuss out her drunk husband.

It was her drunk husband who
thought wife–raping was a
weekend sport.

When he was in the woods she
painted sunny little watercolors
of Venice, blue canals and
yellow sloping bridges.

Mollie Poupeney

Fern

I don't suppose you remember
the Indian girl that lived
in that trailer behind you?
She and me'd get together
sometimes and canned salmon.

She loved home brew, used
to run her head right into
a tree when she had a little
too much— Indians do that,
you know.

I hear she had a head–on
collision with a concrete
divider last year,
killed instantly, nine
in the morning

She was cold sober.

She took care of you kids
sometimes.

I liked her, but some people
were kind of funny about
things like that.

Her husband lost his hand
in a saw, cut it clean off
at the wrist— not in the woods.
Table saw of some kind making
a knicknack shelf for her living
room. Big Swede.

You can't beat home brew.

Mollie Poupeney

Mutt

The sun was so hot
on the beach and you
kids got bad sunburns,
peeled like two tomatoes
and went right back out and
got bad sunburns again. Your
little brother blistered so
bad he had sacks of water hanging
from his skinny little back.
You got bad boils on yours.

Your mama put butter and cream
from the top of the milk
bottle on you but it didn't
help none, so she took you
to our trailer and put you on
our bed and Phinola, she put her
knees on your fanny to hold
you down.

She pressed and squeezed until she
got them cores out. You was hollering
"Help! Murder! Police! They're
killing me!"

You got that out of the funny
papers, I guess. They used to
say things like that.

Your mama almost fainted, I remember
that much.

Mollie Poupeney

Mutt Smith

Your little brother
never could say her
name, Phinola, so he
called her Shinola.
She called him her
little papoose.

Now she's gone.

Mollie Poupeney

Wooden Eye Wilson

It was against the rules to have
any booze in camp, but it was getting
along toward Fourth of July and me and
your dad decided to walk the tracks to
a bootlegger we knew had a place a few
miles down on the highway so's we could
get a head start on the weekend fireworks.
We went right from work so we was
wearing our corks, and we each bought
two gallon jugs and headed back up the
track. Well, carrying them bottles
got kind of awkward, and we had ourselves
a little nip along the way. Then Smokey
decides it would be easier to slip his
belt through the handles on the jugs
and carry them on his hips so's he could show
me how good he could walk the rails in
his cork boots. He was always real agile
on his feet, and prided himself how he could
do special stunts in his corks, jumping windfalls
or from one stump to another in the woods. One
time I remember he took a running start and ran
ten feet up the trunk of an old hemlock, but I
told him it wasn't the same trying to balance on
them iron rails with them iron nails in the soles,
but he did it anyhow to show me how wrong I was.

He did it so good, walking that rail with
his arms out like he was on a tightrope, them two
jugs hanging from his hips, that he decided he
could jump from one rail to the other and
back. He did it once, and the second time,
down he went on that iron rail right on his
hip and there went his two gallons of whiskey
all over the tracks. He cusses a blue streak,
then he starts laughing along with me.

By the time we get back to camp there ain't
too much left in one of my gallons either,
but by that time it don't much matter, we
had a hell of a time!

Mollie Poupeney

Cougar Bill

We was all straggling into camp
one Sunday night and I was walking
toward the tramway when I seen your
Uncle Dave's car on the tram with
his wheel over the edge, hanging
over the swampwater. Well, he was
cussing and looking at the wheel
and I could tell he was drunkern
he probably should be, so I pretend
I don't see him, kinda shy the
other way in the dark, when he hears
me and wants to know where the hell
do I think I'm going.

I say, well, Dave, I see you're
having a little trouble and I figure
I would go get a few of the boys
to give you a hand, and he says,

It only took one man to get the
goddam thing off the tram, so two
men should be plenty to get the
goddam thing back on.

Well, I knew we couldn't do no
such a thing, but I went back and
tried, that's how convincing your
uncle was, drunk or sober.

Mollie Poupeney

Elaine

Your dad said one time
what did I want to do
with my life and I said
I could be happy anywhere
and he said I'd be a good
person to be in jail with

Mollie Poupeney

Ramona

She lies sick on her
hideabed and asks is
my mother still living,
and recalls how we all
took the logging train
to the top of the ridge
to pick blackberries.

My legs sting remembering
the tangled briars that
cut through my overalls
and left scratches like
red ink lines that wouldn't
wash off in Saturday night
bathwater, would burn worse
than too much black pepper in
the navy bean soup—

She said that old One Spot
engine climbed and twisted
around them ridges like a
snake with rocks on its back,
and I smell the scorch of
hot sap in sawdust, and hear
the wailing highlead and the
scream of the steam donkey.

Your mother made enough
blackberry jam to last the
whole winter, she said.

Your daddy was one hundred
per cent man; your folks
was older'n me, just married
and with a new baby.

You looked just like a famous
movie star, I tell her. Jean
Harlow didn't hold a candle to you.

You, she smiles, how would you know?
You were just a scabby-kneed kid.

Mollie Poupeney

Little Brother

Your knees were like brown apples
on your skinny little legs.
Your baby teeth chattered when you
asked, do we have to go, and what's
going to happen now to Daddy? I
dropped your hand and ran toward
the ocean. I don't know, I screamed
at the seagulls, I don't know, I
screamed at the wave. I don't know

I screamed at the sun

Mary L. Hanner

The Cabbage Baby

She'd heard about the reliable California sun before she and Leland moved to San Jose from Gatlinburg, Tennessee in April, but no one had told her about the fences, those gray slats of redwood that made a crazyquilt of the suburbs, severing her world at about six feet.

"They're for privacy," Leland told her, but she wondered why people needed so much privacy in California. Did they walk around naked behind those boards? Or beat the children there so no one could see? Glenda and Leland had nothing to hide behind their fence. Fully dressed, they grilled hamburgers on hot, still summer evenings, and they didn't have children, at least not yet.

Glenda put Grandma's hickory rocker in the middle of the concrete patio, and that's where she spent August, the third month of her first pregnancy. Glenda remembered her grandmother with stick–thin legs, sitting in the rocking chair on the porch in Gatlinburg, rocking and watching Clingman's Dome, the highest peak of the Great Smokies. Grandma said there were secrets in them mountains and it was a girl's job in life to find them out. You'd think it wouldn't have hurt if she'd leaned down and whispered just one secret to Glenda, sprawled on the old woman's lap until Mama said she'd break both Grandma's legs if she sat in her lap many more years. So here was Glenda, pregnant in California, and she didn't know anything.

Grandma wouldn't like California. She wouldn't be able to see green mountains to the east, or the sun come up in long pearl–pink fingers every morning. Not that Grandma could see anything now, Glenda reminded herself. The old woman hadn't exactly died, she just stopped one day. She must have been a hundred, and Mama said it was for the best.

Grandma would have liked the garden. Glenda folded her hands over her stomach and considered the vegetable patch she and Leland had planted in May. Lettuce and radishes were due for replanting, watermelon peered out from under green umbrella leaves, the carrots were doing poorly, and the cabbages were ready. Yesterday Leland had brought three cabbages from the garden and set them on the picnic bench.

"They boil up better if you leave 'em in the night air awhile," he'd told her.

Glenda rocked and thought about cabbages, babies, her backyard world of gray and blue and a little green, and the other pregnant women she'd met in the doctor's office. The women had talked about breech deliveries, episiotomies and morning sickness. Glenda hadn't had any of those things. She decided she knew mostly about boiling new cabbage with that leftover wedge of ham and a couple small onions. They would eat it with butter and milk. Her mouth watered, but the cabbages needed their night air. She would have to wait a few days.

Those days were enough time to lose the baby, days that would stretch out in her memory like dying itself, gray and inescapable. She wasn't even sure when it happened exactly. She didn't just stop being pregnant that afternoon but something must have happened between the time she stopped to pull snails from the anemic ivy near the fence and Leland's arrival home from the supermarket where he worked as a butcher. She began to bleed.

She searched the closet for a box and found one, a shoe box with "Super Keds, What America Grows In," printed in black letters on the side. She strained pale slivers of tissue from the toilet bowl to bury in the box out by the ivy because it wasn't right to flush the toilet and let go of a baby, even a baby that was only a picture in her mind, a soft picture without many edges.

She stood there by the fence and shivered like a puppy while she dug and sang the only song she could remember at the moment, "Away in a manger, no crib...", over and over. She didn't sing it loud, of course. The neighbors might hear. And she never got beyond the word 'crib.' The words seemed to stop in her mouth at that point, just stop for no reason at all, even though she'd sung that song for as long as she could remember. The green of the ivy swam, and she thought she tasted dirt where she lay unable to move that afternoon. The good neighbor fence hid her. Glenda guessed she'd die there, her life draining out of her like Grandma's treacle from the metal tin.

She didn't die. She spent three days in the hospital lying between stiff white sheets and watching "soaps", as her roommate called them. The doctor said Glenda had lost a lot of blood and needed to rest. There would be other babies, he assured her. Leland didn't cry. Tennessee men don't cry. Glenda tried not to.

"What were you doin' out there with the shovel and all?" Leland asked her.

"Buryin'."

There had been other buryings, ones she couldn't remember. Mama took her down to the corner of the wood once and showed her a circle of stones where three babies were buried, two of Glenda's brothers and one sister. She thought about those babies as a circle of granite under the pines and a certain way Mama looked whenever she passed the tiny cemetary.

"Don't be sad," Mama had said. "Them babies musta done what they were supposed to and didn't need all this trouble any more."

The cabbages were gone when Glenda came home from the hospital.

"Rotted," Leland told her. "Too much night air. I forgot about them, what with you and the baby..."

So she rocked anyway while August turned into September, but it was hard to tell when that happened in California. She no longer heard the sounds of children behind the fences. School must have started.

From the little garden they brought in more tomatoes, squash, melon and cabbages than they could eat. Glenda carried a box of vegetables next door where a young girl with cranky yellow hair and hooded eyes answered the door, opening it only enough to receive the cardboard box, with no thanks. This wasn't Tennessee. This was California.

"God's own earth," Leland said, holding up a zucchini squash nearly as long as his arm. "You stick any old seed in the ground and sure enough, it grows."

But not always, Glenda thought. She needed something that was for always, so they bought three mournful red boulders to place in the garden by the fence.

"Why do you want them three ol' rocks?" he asked her at the rockery where she bent down and stared at each stone for a long time.

"They got secrets. You see that one? Looks like Clingman's Dome, don't it?"

He shook his head slowly. "The Dome was awful spooky. Wouldn't even grow pines."

"I'm going home someday," Glenda told him, "and I'm gonna climb up there. I'm gonna see for myself."

"What'd you do with those cabbages that rotted?" she asked him when the three rocks were in place by the fence. "You know, the ones you said needed night air and got too much.'

"I threw 'em under the ivy.'

She stared at him.

"You see how green that ivy got? I wouldn't be a bit surprised come next spring those old cabbages took root and grew. Like I said, you put it in the ground in California, and darned if it don't grow into something."

But not always, she knew. Not even in California.

Dorothy A. Stroup
Dragonflies and Autumn Grass

It is quite appropriate that Mr. Uematsu's name means "top of the pine tree" or maybe "above the pine tree." He organized our haiku translating society in Hiroshima, and sometimes he acted very much like his name, looking down on us from above. At moments, when he was trying to move us around like chess pieces, he seemed to be operating from a spot even higher than the pine tree. But of course he knew what he was about more than the others. The rest of us, especially the foreigners, were rather naively pleased with our translations and with ourselves. Mr. Uematsu never was. He and I were English teachers at the Women's College, but he had been graduated from both Japanese and American universities in both Japanese and English literature, and he knew that the gap between Shakespeare and Bashō was very wide. He knew that summer days in England were soft and warm, that Japan's were hot and sticky and unbearable, and that a Japanese poet would not compare a summer day to a lovely girl. The only thing most of us foreigners knew about haiku was that it contained 17 syllables. But we found out, during the year, that there was more to know.

"Well, now, that's a rather decent translation," Mr. Garnell would say cheerfully after the Japanese had finally come to some kind of uneasy agreement about the meaning, and after we had selected what we thought were the most precise words in the English language. He had been sent by the British Council to teach English at Hiroshima University, and he was a writer himself. We would bathe for a moment in his sunny English smile. But then we would catch a glimpse of Mr. Uematsu, smothering the scowl on his face, clamping down hard on his smokeless briar pipe.

"I repeat," he would say, taking his pipe out of his mouth and jabbing it at all of us in general, "it is not the words we care for. It is not the literal thing. It is the *feeling*. We have lost the *feeling!*"

Part of the problem was that we conjured up separate visual images. Take dragonflies, for instance. We had been trying to translate a haiku about a little boy chasing dragonflies, his cheeks glistening from having cried a moment before. Mr. Uematsu didn't want to use the word dragonfly for the Japanese word, *tonbo*. After all, he said, a dragon in the west is legendary and exotic, isn't it? So the English word carries those connotations, too. Not so with *tonbo*. The childhood of every Japanese is smeared with images of *tonbo*—chasing them, catching them sometimes, keeping them imprisoned, letting them go. The word is fraught with daily contact and intimacy. Besides, he said, the dragonflies he had seen in America were different. They were smaller and they weren't the same color.

I didn't understand until a year later when I was walking along a river at the edge of a rice field in late August and directly encountered a *tonbo* myself. It was quivering on a rock. Its red wings, unfolding and catching the glints of the sun, were covered with a delicate, baby–down fuzz so light that it did not affect the transparency. It was ethereal, evanescent, and yet, somehow, pettable. In my own childhood, in America, dragonflies were only slightly more fascinating than lady bugs.

But anyway, there isn't any other word in English. "Dragonflies" is all we've got.

And that wasn't the only problem. There were cherry blossoms, too. They were a problem not because they looked different, but because for more than a thousand years, Japanese poetry has focused on that particular symbol of evanescence. To get through to a real cherry blossom, the Japanese have to unwrap layers of profundities, images, echoes, memories, scraps of poetry, associate words that adhere like adhesive tape to the original word, visions of painted handscrolls, patterns on a kimono, on tea cups, on sliding doors. We foreigners, for the most part, could just shut our eyes and see a cherry blossom.

Another problem was that, although Mr. Uematsu struggled as hard as the rest of us to get a perfect translation, his dissatisfaction with our failure was not a source of sorrow for him. He took pleasure in it, for he had revealed that our haiku society was organized partly out of a desire for revenge.

In fact, the society was the direct result of a study group formed by the English teachers at the college to read modern American fiction. I was the only native speaker in the group, and the others were always pressing me to explain shades of meaning which I didn't understand myself. Once toward the end of the school year, we came across "Powerhouse," a story by Eudora Welty, which was full of the dialogue of black musicians. After we read it, Mr. Uematsu found a critical essay that said the whole story was a symphony and that the sentences, issued spontaneously by the musicians, had the rhythm and beat of a jazz band. It was the last straw, he said. He couldn't catch the lilt of inflection and the underlying meaning in the dialogues of Philip Roth's New Jersey Jewish aunts, or J.D. Salinger's sibling conversations, or the tone or even the whole point of Richard Brautigan's *Trout Fishing in America.* If he couldn't understand it, he said, how could he teach it to his students? He had studied English for twenty years, he said, and instead of going forward, he was regressing. Mark Twain, Bret Harte, Stephen Crane. They were no problem. Even Henry James. In fact, he had thought he was making some progress with Faulkner. But now they were pulling the modern language out from under his feet like a rug.

There was really nothing the rest of us could say. We disbanded our study group for the summer, and in the fall, when Mr. Uematsu came to the foreign residence where I lived, he proposed that we give up the study group altogether and form a haiku translating society instead. "More people will be interested," he said, "not just English teachers. We can invite Japanese, Americans, English."

"But none of the foreigners are good enough for that," I protested. "Except maybe George Garnell."

"It's all right," he said. "We can explain it to you. All you have to do is find the best English word."

I was quite excited. "Maybe if we're really good, we can publish," I said.

Mr. Uematsu smiled condescendingly. "That," he said, "is highly unlikely." He was puffing intermittently on his briar pipe, although as usual there was only an ember in the bowl and no smoke coming out. He was always jabbing his pipe in the air or biting down hard on the stem as if forcing higher voltage into the already electric wire of himself.

In those days his hair was always just long enough to make him stand out in a subway crowd. No one was ever sure whether he kept it purposely long, or whether he just forgot to get it cut. He was forever flinging it back out of the way with a quick jerk of his head.

"Maybe we won't publish," he said, "but at least you might be able to understand better the Japanese heart."

His hair had just crept back over his eyes, so I couldn't tell whether he was being serious or sardonic. I never really knew what Mr. Uemstsu was all about anyway. When I first saw him, standing in the middle of the living room floor, hollow–cheeked, his back curved into a slight bend as if he were part of a flower arrangement, I thought he had just stepped out of an old Samurai movie. And I don't mean Toshiro Mifune. I mean the sensitive, delicate one who dies of consumption before he gets to take part in the revenge. In those days I thought of Mr. Uematsu as typically Japanese. But he wasn't typical at all. Of anything. There was the briar pipe and his fluent English. But the pipe was actually made in Japan, and the English, usually impeccable, carried a Japanese syntactical ring.

He finally jerked his hair back out of his face and looked at me straight on.

"Do you know the real reason for the society?" he asked.

I didn't answer. I just looked at him expectantly.

"It's our way of getting back at you. For Eudora Welty." He paused to let that sink in. "I want to see if the frustration works the other way. I want to know if you are as much at ocean as we are."

"But Uematsu–*sensei*," I protested, (*sensei* means teacher in Japanese, and it is a term of respect) "we don't know Japanese the way you know English. That's not fair."

"No, no," he said. "It's not a test of proficiency in the language." He stood up. "You'll see when we get started." Then he left.

I didn't see when we got started. The early meetings were merely pleasant social gatherings. We held them in the foreign residence and served lots of tea and cookies, which got more attention than the haiku. But Mr. Uematsu persisted. He had picked the poet, Teijo Nakamura, a woman born in 1901, and still writing haiku and living in Yokohama. Every session he would choose three or four haiku suitable to the season, and make copies for everyone in both Japanese characters and Roman letters, leaving ample room for doodling. Then, after he read the poem in Japanese and gave rough word–for–word translations in English, he and the other Japanese would explain the nuances, sometimes for an hour. We would argue over the choice of English words and eventually agree somehow on a final version. The Japanese deferred politely to the foreigners on points of English, and besides, because we had invited everyone we knew while Mr. Uematsu had limited the Japanese side, they were outnumbered, outvoiced, and sometimes ignored by us. It made us arrogant in our ignorance.

Gradually the novelty wore off and the foreigners began to dwindle. Of course I hung on, along with the two other American teachers, mostly because we all lived where the meetings were held. But the most valuable foreigner, Mr. Garnell, who had written poetry himself, stayed on. He was the only one among us who had studied Japanese literature and he wouldn't accept a translation that was done for the feeling alone, as Mr. Uematsu kept exhorting us to do. He was our watchdog for scholarly precision, and he sometimes got quietly impatient with us. We could always tell when he was irritated because he would retreat into a corner and translate the haiku he fancied into Latin, which he said was more faithful to the original, anyway.

The rest of us were pretty peripheral, even expendable. The few American teachers, Navy officers and wives from the military base near Hiroshima came mostly out of curiosity, and usually didn't last after the first few sessions. The people from the Atomic Bomb Casualty Commission at Hijiyama in Hiroshima lasted longer, but they eventually faded too, except for Dr. Eckelsberg and his wife, Sally, who kept coming until the very end. He had finished his last year of internship, and they had just married.

They liked the haiku meetings better than anyone. They kept translating the haiku into neat little synthetic English pearls—tiny jeweled microcosms that matched their image of Japan. They couldn't understand why we seldom accepted their submissions as the final version.

That was the foreign side. The Japanese side, from the beginning, had been smaller, but more consistent. There were two high school English teachers, recent graduates of the Women's College, who said they enjoyed the meetings immensely, but they exhibited this mostly by giggling from behind the backs of their hands. Mr. Uematsu's two colleagues from the Women's College were Mr. Kiyama, who usually fell asleep before the meeting was over, and Mr. Okamoto, who, during the early sessions, sat quietly and smiled without saying anything. He was to become more vociferous later when he led the faction supporting the classical view.

The other Japanese who came—college students, teachers who had been in the study group and teachers from other high schools and colleges, graduate students at the University—appeared off and on throughout the year, invited by someone. But like the foreigners, they came at first with high enthusiasm, and then after a few sessions, disappeared. It was Mr. Uematsu, alone most of the time (Mr. Kiyama helped when he wasn't asleep), explaining haiku to the foreigners, and he couldn't even make a dent in our thick skulls because we thought, all through that early period, that we were actually translating haiku.

Miss Taki was the first one to change things. A young university instructor had brought her, and although he didn't come again, Miss Taki was present at every session until the end. She was rumored to be writing a brilliant M.A. thesis on T.S. Eliot, but this information was difficult to pin down because Miss Taki didn't talk about herself. She was too busy observing protocol. When she was late, which was her usual situation, she crept into the room behind the chairs of her superiors at the university, and behind anybody who could, by the most distant application, hold claim to the title of *Sensei*. We always looked forward a little to her entrances because she was much more noticeable, pushing her way between the wall and the chairs to get to an empty seat, than she would have been just walking in front of everybody. We pretended not to notice her until she had been sitting in her seat for a while, or until she said something about the haiku.

"Oh, nice to see you, Miss Taki," one of us would finally say. She would nod her head slightly. "Eh," she would say in that gentle, vague, but abrupt way Japanese women have for ending a conversation that might draw too much attention to themselves. Her stern singleness of purpose seriously dampened our frivolity. Probably she caused the final exodus of the American military.

When she didn't like one of the poems, she said so, and told us why. She told us if she thought the feeling was grotesque or the image trite. Mr. Uematsu had always carefully refrained from influencing our aesthetic judgment. Now, at least, there was someone who could tell us how we *ought* to feel.

When we translated a haiku about cherry blossoms seeming to linger for a moment in mid air before they fell to the ground, I was enchanted by it. It was the first time that I really felt in tune with the poet's vision. Everybody else liked it too. Mr. Okamoto said it was the first superior haiku we had come across. Sally Eckelsberg said she thought it was typically Japanese.

Miss Taki said that, on the contrary, she thought it was unbelievably trite: "It is very dangerous to use the cherry blossom in a poem," she said quietly, primly. "It is the most challenging task for all poets," she said, "because we have used it and used it and used it."

Mr. Okamoto accused Miss Taki of using English standards for judging Japanese poetry. "That is the beauty of our poetry," he said. "We use it and use it and use it. It is the iceberg. You merely say the word, and it echoes, reverberates, down deep inside the soul. That is the point. It is not simply this one poem about the cherry blossoms, but all the poems, all the way back to the *Manyoshu*, our most ancient book of poetry."

Miss Taki, who by this time was talking in Japanese, translated into rapid–fire English by Mr. Uematsu, said that there were better poems for expressing such a situation. There were so many, in fact, that she didn't see the need for creating another one.

Mr. Okamoto said that he thought the poem perfectly brought together an ancient and modern sentiment.

"Miss Taki has just told Mr. Okamoto..." Mr. Uematsu was saying. Then, "Mr. Okamoto has just told Miss Taki that..."

Mr. Garnell interrupted him. "Falling cherry petals linger in mid air," he said brightly, trying to stop the argument and get the discussion back to the translation. "How's that?"

They ignored him. They were talking so fast that Mr. Uematsu gave up translating. "It is not an interesting argument any more," he told us. "It is not worth translating."

It was the first time the Japanese had kept the floor for more than a sentence. I began to get more interested in the haiku than in the tea. But I had the uneasy, hollow feeling that my center of gravity was being shifted.

Even so, our opaque understanding continued to cause greater distress to Mr. Uematsu than it did to us. There was the *chindonya*, for instance, a man who walks about the streets advertising a restaurant or noodle shop, beating some kind of percussion instrument and wearing a sandwich–style sign.

"Oh, you mean like 'Eat at Joe's?'" Dr. Eckeslberg asked.

Mr. Uematsu winced with pain. It was far, he said, oh, so far from that. How could he explain, he wondered. What could he compare it with that would make it adequate to our imagination? He looked around for help. Mr. Kiyama woke up and gazed at the floor. Mr. Okamoto said there weren't many *chindonya–sans* these days, especially in Hiroshima. One of the high school teachers said maybe they were closer to clowns. Mr. Uematsu refused to accept that, too. We looked at Miss Taki. Miss Taki looked at her doodle sheet.

Finally Mr. Uematsu said that the word *chindonya* came from the bell–like sound their percussion instruments made. That was the important element, not the sandwich signs, which they didn't always wear. It was a tradition that reached way back. They had advertised temple festivals in ancient times, and they painted their faces and wore different kinds of hats and clothes, and sometimes they danced, and it was a profession, not a job—but different from the profession of a clown.

We looked up *chindonya* in Kenkyusha's Japanese–English dictionary, and it said, "a ding–dong party for publicity; a public–

ity agent with bugles, drums and comic dances." That didn't help. It wasn't as good as Mr. Uematsu's explanation.

We settled on street crier, but it wasn't right. Mr. Uematsu let the black shank of his hair fall down over his eyes, and rolled his head dolefully back and forth, not saying anything.

Once we were translating a haiku about a mother and child standing outside in the cold under a lantern with their heads bent. I didn't understand why anybody would write a poem about that.

"Here. Right here," Mr. Uematsu said, thumping the back of his neck. "What do you call that?" he demanded. He was singularly unsatisfied with "nape of the neck." He and the other Japanese were appalled that there was no single noun in English for what they said was the most beautiful part of a woman's body.

"Nape of the neck!" Mr. Uematsu exclaimed in disgust.

The Japanese have a beautiful, soft word for it—*unaji*.

"Their bare necks," we tried. We tried simply "nape" without the neck. "Bending their heads." Nothing would really do. There was no way of expressing something English speakers had never perceived. Mr. Uematsu began muttering something about needing outside help. But it wasn't until after the haiku about the train smoke that he finally did anything. That haiku needed quite a lot of explaining before we could understand it.

mugi no me ni Rye's sprouts in	(The *no* is a possessive which makes *mugi* (rye) the owner of *me* (sprouts). The *ni* means "in" or "within" or "among." But in Japanese the word order is different. The English would be "in the sprouts of rye.")
Kisha no kemui no train's smoke's	(Of course, instead of "train's smoke's touch", we would say "a touch of train smoke.")
sawari kiyu touch vanishes	

So: In the sprouts of rye, a touch of train smoke vanishes.

Mr. Uematsu described a train streaking across a rye field leaving behind a cloud of smoke that was seen for only an instant before it vanished. It reminded me of Kansas, of course. But I had thought, in my own mind, that the train had stopped in a station and emitted smoke on a tiny clump of rye sprouts, obliterating them for a moment. Mr. Uematsu's version, it turned out, was more Kansan than mine. A whole field of rye instead of a tiny Japanese clump.

Mr. Uematsu commented on the contrast of dark train smoke and the young buds of rye in the spring.

"Oh," said Sally Eckelsberg, "like English protest poetry against the industrial revolution."

Mr. Uematsu gave her his blank attention.

"In the nineteenth century," she added.

"Well, it's even more applicable today," said her husband. "Ecology and all that."

Mr. Uematsu took his pipe out of his mouth and cleared his throat. We all waited awhile for something to come out. I knew that he was telling himself to be calm and patient and understanding. "Well, now," he said, after he'd taken a deep breath, "perhaps it may be compared to that." He took another breath and then smiled benignly. He said he thought there was a feeling about old steam trains in Japan which western people didn't seem to have. He said the Japanese traveled on them and revered them and looked at them with awe. In the past, there had never been any strong aversion toward the train.

"Well, what about those rapid bullet trains?" asked Sally. "Everybody's always complaining about them and having aversions toward them."

"*Yes*! Those evil monsters extending their tentacles across Japan and choking out all of our lives!" He seemed for a moment to have forgotten the subject.

"See!" said Sally. "You all *do* have aversions."

"But that's *different*!" He was pretty irritated by now. "Teijo Nakamura wrote that poem long before there was any rapid bullet train in Japan. And she wasn't protesting anything, particularly. It was just a pleasant image—the streak of the train cutting a line through the wheat field. That's all. And then a puff of smoke as an afterthought. Or maybe it's like an exclamation point at the end of a sentence."

Sally was nodding meekly in agreement now, but he wasn't finished.

"That's all we need from haiku, you know," he said, "just a picture or an image. Not a message. Of course, sometimes, it can suggest other profundities, but that is not necessary. And a message is *never* necessary!" He was pounding his fist on his knee. "*Never* a message!" he said again. Dr. Eckeslberg interrupted what might have been his third re–statement. "Well, how about 'a touch of smoke disappears into the rye field after the train goes by'?" he asked. He tried to sit out the silence that followed but he couldn't. "Well, what about that?"

Mr. Garnell finally cleared his throat. "Well," he ventured delicately, "it should sound a *bit* like poetry, shouldn't it?"

"And besides," said Miss Taki, "in the original, there is no field and no moving train. We must try to be faithful."

"But otherwise I don't get what it means," he said. "I never understand it."

I looked at Mr. Uematsu. He was glowing. "Yes," he said with an elaborate air, "we Japanese often have that problem with English." He grinned at me. I did not grin back.

"Well, but how are we going to translate it, then?" asked Jim Eckelsberg, not at all put off by the sympathy.

Mr. Garnell suggested "puff" to convey the evanescence, and "tender rye" instead of sprouts. It had a better sense of a field, he thought.

I read out his version: "A puff of train smoke vanishes in the tender rye."

One of the other American teachers said she didn't like the "puff". It was even farther from the meaning than "touch", she thought.

"Caress?" Miss Taki asked.

Hmm. Nobody accepted it. But nobody rejected it, either.

Jim was still disgruntled. If the train was moving through a field, as everybody seemed to think, then why couldn't we just say so? He looked around the room for somebody who might be reasonable enough to answer his question. Mr. Uematsu was sitting soberly, trying to formulate an answer, but before he could speak, Mr. Okamoto asked everybody where they thought the poet was when she wrote the haiku. Was she standing in the field of rye? What would Teijo Nakamura be doing in a field of rye? Of course she would be sitting on a train.

"No," Mr. Uematsu argued, "then the whole image of a train streaking across a field is lost." And of course, he said, Mrs. Nakamura could be standing in a field of rye. Maybe she had been born on a farm. Maybe she had a country house. Could Mr. Okamoto prove that she didn't? Besides, it wasn't fair, bringing a poet's personal life into her poems.

Miss Taki said that since the Japanese didn't indicate where the poet was, the English shouldn't either, and so what was the point of arguing?

"But we've got to have *some* information," said Jim.

Mr. Okamoto went on speaking. He addressed Mr. Uematsu in Japanese, and it was as if Jim and Miss Taki were in another world, not even visible. He said sitting on a train looking at a puff of smoke was certainly worthy of haiku. He'd done it. He'd seen smoke from the engine disappear just when it reached the window where he was sitting. it was much more immediate than standing in a field watching the train go by. And he was not bringing Mrs. Nakamura's personal life into it. He was thinking of his own experience.

He looked around at us for a reaction, but we all sat transfixed by the transformation from silent, placid Mr. Okamoto to opinionated, protesting Mr. Okamoto. He looked a little surprised himself. Then, in the middle of the ensuing silence he said it looked to him as if it were going to rain, and he'd like to get home before the downpour, since he had come on his bicycle. Mr. Kiyama woke up suddenly and said he thought he should go too. They both left abruptly.

Only Mr. Uematsu stayed for tea, although the Eckelsbergs hung around for a while to say that they thought the English language couldn't stand as much vagueness as the Japanese. They said that without an explanation the final version was useless. They were very discouraged. Mr. Uematsu said he was glad they were beginning to see some of the problems. Somehow that seemed to make them feel better and they left.

During tea, Mr. Uematsu told us he would have to get help. He couldn't explain things to us well enough. Besides, he needed more support if he was going to have to argue with Mr. Okamoto.

To the next session, he brought Professor Hideo Kata who taught English literature at Hiroshima University. His tastes leaned heavily toward the Picaresque and the Gothic. That night, we translated a haiku about a winter bee at the window of a vacant house, bathed in sunshine. Maybe, Mr. Kata suggested, the house wasn't just empty because everyone was gone on an afternoon shopping tour, as we had all supposed. Maybe the house was haunted. I had a momentary vision of Mr. Kata's house with a heavy wind howling outside, and stained glass windows adorned by dusty velvet curtains. I couldn't get rid of it. I had been trying to see a Japanese house. But the Gothic castle stuck with all of us and we finally had to give up the translation.

Another time we were doing a haiku about a shooting star, just outside the window, that had burned itself out. Professor Kata said the star was passion—love passion, of course, burning itself out unto death. "All the way aflame," he wanted to translate it. It was as if the romanticism flowed, unchecked, through his veins.

There was a strange poem about someone being sick in bed and being suddenly aware of the warmth of the ring on her finger. The woman missed her lover, Mr. Kata said, and it was the memory of him, not the ring itself, which brought the warmth.

Mr. Uematsu was beginning to lose his patience. He didn't see it that way at all, he said. It's just that things are distorted when you're sick. Didn't anybody remember how it was being in bed with a fever? Shadows were bigger. Things were unreal. So the heat of the metal, intensified by the fever, was unreal too.

Mr. Okamoto agreed with Mr. Kata but he didn't think it was necessary to emphasize the love element. It could be any sentimental attachment. The important thing was that the ring did not carry an ordinary physical warmth. It was the warmth of the heart, of sentiment, of lingering memories and languor. Writing a haiku about a ring that was hot just because a person had a fever was not poetic. The whole idea was too scientific.

Mr. Uematsu didn't speak until he had laid his pipe down carefully on the table and then gripped both sides of his arm chair as if he were on a plane making an emergency landing.

"What is the whole point of haiku, anyway?" he asked reasonably, quietly. We did not venture to answer his rhetorical question. We knew that his calmness was a thin veneer covering his agitated self. So we listened attentively as he continued to frame his argument in the shape of rhetorical questions. Wasn't the point, he said, to perceive the profound and universal in simple, everyday things that were not romantic or poetic of themselves? What about Bashō cooling his heels against the wall while taking an afternoon nap, or Buson examining the belly of a frog? Was that poetic? Was anything Basho wrote, of itself, poetic?

"Of course!" Mr. Okamoto was almost shouting. "He wrote about the smell of the plum blossoms, the cry of the heron at night, the voice of the cicada."

"The cicada is an ordinary, common Japanese insect!" Mr. Uematsu was finally shouting too. He ignored the other examples. "It is poetic because Bashō made it so."

Mr. Garnell had to wave his hands around and shout a bit to get the floor. Even when he got it, the debate team was annoyed. Wasn't it better, Mr. Garnell asked, to get two interpretations out of a poem than just one anyway? To wonder whether the poet was thinking about her lover, or just had a fever?

"That's MY argument," said Miss Taki indignantly.

We tried to get back to the translation, but we couldn't.

Mr. Uematsu brought Yoshi Katayuki to the next meeting. He didn't know anything about English literature. He didn't even speak English. Yoshi composed music. He was especially interested in string instruments. He played the violin and liked Bach. But he had a deeper inclination toward the *koto*, the *biwa*, and the *samisen*, and these were the instruments that he taught. He had a preference for ancient court music, and the music of Noh dramas.

His first haiku evening, Mr. Kata and Mr. Okamoto got into an argument over the source of an archaic word the poet had used. They were discussing which classical Japanese poem she might be alluding to. The argument had gone on so long that Mr. Uematsu had given up translating for us, and we were all sitting, politely, waiting for them to finish. Yoshi sat in his tastefully hand–woven kimono, his arms folded in front of him, inside his sleeves, alert and listening, moving his head back and forth so that he could gaze on the face of each speaker in turn.

In the middle of following the conversation, he suddenly unleashed a flood of laughter. Oh, but he wasn't laughing at the professors, of course, he hastened to assure us. He had allowed his mind to wander. Forgive him.

It was rude. He had been thinking of something one of his pupils had said that morning. He didn't offer to tell us what it was. But the discussion ended without any particular conclusion.

The next time he came we translated a haiku about a dark mirror, clouded with the white breath of the poet. Mr. Okamoto said he liked the poem very much. He liked the contrast of the outward purity symbolized by the white breath, and an inner dark soul symbolized by the mirror.

Mr. Uematsu bit down hard, glumly, on his pipe. Mr. Garnell shifted uneasily. He said that however rampant the "dark soul" implications were in western literature, he certainly never had the impression they existed in Japanese. He had always found a refreshing lack of Puritanism in the literature he read, and he did not think the haiku should be burdened with a heavy–handed interpretation like that. Wasn't the poet just contrasting light and dark because of her interest in color?

Miss Taki lifted her gaze from the doodle sheet to the people, a rare moment. The interpretation, she said, was neither as heavy as Mr. Okamoto's nor as flat as Mr. Garnell's. After all, you could interpret lightness and darkness in many ways. Maybe it was the poet's mood that was dark, not her soul.

We were silent, implying agreement.

"Breath whitens the dark mirror as I draw it close," Mr. Garnell stabbed into the silence. Doesn't sound quite proper in English, does it?

"Maybe we should just keep the same order as the Japanese," he said, after thinking a little longer.

> "On the dark mirror
> drawn close—
> breath whitens"

They both sounded o.k. to me. "Where's the seasonal word?" I asked. Mr. Uematsu had told us that it is essential to the interpretation of the poem to find the seasonal word. Sometimes it is quite easy, as in "autumn grass" and "spring rains", or with cherry blossoms and snow. But at other times, as in the case of the shooting star, you can't be sure, and ultimately, if nobody knows, you have to look it up in a book that tells you once and for all. Mr. Uematsu didn't like to use the book. He usually trusted in his own instincts. He fixed me with a firm gaze and asked me if I'd ever seen white breath on a mirror or a window pane in any season besides winter.

I considered kicking him. I was getting pretty tired of his "let's be patient with the foreigners" tone. I hadn't treated *him* like that when I was explaining things to the study group.

Jim Eckelsberg suggested "frost" or "frozen breath" to account for the seasonal word. It seemed reasonable enough, but we couldn't make it fit. We sat enveloped in separate shrouds of silence. Finally, Mr. Kata asked why everybody thought the poet was alone. Couldn't there have been two people in the room? The lover holding up the mirror and gazing at the poet's or the geisha's face while she looked at her own dark reflection?

> Hand it to me
> The dark mirror
> My breath clouds it

That was the way he wanted to translate it. Nobody argued with him. It was pure, florid, velvet. Kata style. We just let it hang there in the air, not wanting to destroy its mood. Then Yoshi laughed again. He was consumed by a series of guffaws that made him roll back and forth on the sofa, hitting Miss Taki on one side of him, and me on the other.

Maybe the whole thing was a joke, he told Mr. Uematsu, who told us in English. The poet wasn't talking about purity and dark souls or black moods at all. She was writing about a geisha combing her hair and dropping dandruff on the mirror. He erupted again at the thought of it. That's all it was, he said. It wasn't breath at all. Just dandruff. He had another attack of laughter. Those geishas, he said, recovering a little and then hiccupping, they've got PILES of dandruff. He clutched his stomach, still guffawing and rolling back and forth, which forced Miss Taki and me to move farther afield, but on her way, Miss Taki slapped a dainty palm over the front of her mouth to keep from revealing her gold inlay and an excess of mirth. It was infectious. Finally we were all giggling helplessly. We couldn't get back to the dark mirror again, so we drank tea instead.

It seemed to me that Uematsu–san was finally satisfied that we had achieved a balance. Therefore I didn't expect the drastic step he took next. He came accompanied by Osamu Hirokawa, a professor who had translated a considerable amount of haiku into English, and had published abroad. He was the one person Mr. Uematsu had ordered us never to invite. He would stifle us, Mr. Uematsu said.

"Well, if someone has to tell you how to feel about haiku, at least he can tell you the right way," Mr. Uematsu explained to me out in the kitchen so that no one could hear.

"But you said he would inhibit us," I whispered.

"No, he won't," Mr. Uematsu said, "He knows we're amateurs. I told him not to expect so much."

"And you're the one who said not to invite him!" I exclaimed.

"Well, that was before I realized how much help I was going to need."

The doorbell rang, and when I came back, Mr. Hirokawa was already sitting in the chair Mr. Uematsu had offered him by the fire. From that time on it was Mr. Hirokawa's chair. He reminded me of a haiku we had once translated about a flame of spring candlelight illuminating someone's cheeks. Mr. Hirakawa's face, under the lamp, and by the firelight, was like that. I remember those silent, thoughtful moments when the air and the doodle sheets were filled with suggestions of English words not yet spoken. I would be watching Mr. Hirokawa's face, all the angles of his nose and chin etched out by the shadows from the lamp, and in the winter, from the fire. His face contained a classical serenity and agelessness that can be found today only in old wood block prints of the Tokugawa era. I would sit, transfixed, comparing his nose to one in Sharaku's prints.

He maintained that changeless, direct continuity with the past despite his modernity and the international recognition he had gained. He had given a series of lectures for the Oriental Languages Department at Yale, and had been offered professorships in Tokyo and several universities in America. But he preferred teaching at a small co–educational college on the outskirts of his native Hiroshima so he could devote more time to his translations and to his own writing. His English vocabulary was dazzling and his accent impeccable. It was a Cambridge accent, not Middle West American.

At Mr. Hirokawa's first meeting, no one had much to say. But as he continued to come, Mr. Okamoto and Mr. Kata grew bolder and began to argue with him. He and Mr. Uematsu usually agreed and supported each other and for a short time Mr. Uematsu seemed quite satisfied. He had almost forgotten about us foreigners, who became more and more accessorial.

But one evening there was mortal combat over a rather pallid haiku about autumn grass. The haiku was written as a kind of question. "Early morning, and who is that, bringing home autumn grass?"

We couldn't agree on anything about it.

Had the poet seen someone's shape so early, probably just at dawn, that the mist was shrouding her view and she couldn't see who it was? Or had she merely seen the traces, the footsteps and leavings of autumn grass that had remained in the morning dew?

The real tension came from the word *akigusa*. Mr. Okamoto said that "autumn grass" was not an adequate translation. In Japanese didn't *akigusa* also mean chrysanthemums and *higanbana* or any of the other typical Japanese autumn flowers? Wasn't there a Chinese allusion to the "seven grasses of autumn" and didn't that mean flowers, not plain old wheat or foxtail or whatever? What was poetic about a farmer bringing a bunch of old grass down from the hills for firewood? Wasn't it rather a delicate female clad in autumn kimono, her arms enfolded around a graceful collection of yellow, violet and amber flowers? It reminded him, he said, of the episode from the Tale of Heike when one of the few survivors of the Heike clan, the mother of the drowned child emperor, had stood among the overgrown thickets at the nunnery to which she had retired, holding a basket of flowers. Tears were streaming down her face, as she stood gazing at her visitor, the retired emperor, the grandfather of her dead child.

It was a convincing argument. I thought everyone would agree with him, and that we would go on with the next haiku. But then Mr. Uematsu erupted.

Why, he asked, did Mr. Okamoto always think that only classical, hackneyed, trite subjects were poetic? Hadn't people chosen, as the generations passed, new subjects to write about? What would it be like if nobody ever wrote any poetry about anything except the Tale of Heike? Did Mr. Okamoto think all modern poetry was bad?

Mr. Kata said that of course Mr. Okamoto was right. Everybody who reads Japanese poetry knows that *kusa*, which usually means grass, meant flowers in this case because it was teamed with the word *aki* (autumn). He had of course been thinking of chrysanthemums when he read the poem and it hadn't occurred to him that anyone, except, of course, the foreigners, would be thinking of anything else, certainly not foxtail or wheat. Were Mr. Hirokawa and Mr. Uematsu actually thinking of foxtail and wheat, he wondered?

Mr. Hirokawa said it would destroy all the freshness of the poem to have to think of a trite Japanese female carrying a dainty handful of flowers. His own vision was of a broad back, a vague form in the distance, carrying an indefinable bundle of something, all so far away in the mist that you couldn't tell who it was or what was being carried. If it were only flowers, you couldn't tell, from that distance, that the person was carrying anythiing at all. Of course it was true that *akigusa* meant "autumn flowers", he said. But it was not always so, and the whole tone of this particular poem led him to believe that no flowers were intended. It was a plain, colloquial-sounding Japanese sentence that ended in a question. Besides, if the poet were close enough to the person to see that it was a woman wearing a kimono and carrying flowers, then she wouldn't have to ask who it was.

Of course she would have to ask, said Mr. Okamoto. If you see someone coming down the street, you can't tell who it is until you get right next to the person.

"You must be very short–sighted, Mr. Okamoto," commented Sally. We giggled. It did not improve his humor.

Mr. Garnell suggested autumn foliage, but then he admitted he didn't like it himself. It didn't satisfy either side.

Mr. Okamoto continued to insist, and Mr. Kata supported him. Mr. Uematsu suggested that we forget the haiku and go on to the next one. It wasn't worth arguing over. Mr. Okamoto accused him of refusing to concede even though he knew he was wrong. Mr. Hirokawa said he didn't think he and Mr. Uematsu were wrong, and that there was no point in continuing the discussion. Mr. Kata agreed. We started to do the next haiku, but Mr. Okamoto wouldn't let us. His arguments, spoken in insisting, demanding Japanese, continued to issue forth. He was annoyed that Mr. Kata had agreed to drop the discussion. Mr. Uematsu refused to translate any more of what he had said. He tried, once more, to read off the new haiku. Mr. Okamoto stood up, wearing an impassive, tightly controlled face, and said he didn't want to translate any more haiku that night or any other time ever. He stuffed his doodle sheets into his pocket and walked out the door. We barely had time to go to the front entrance with him and bow.

He didn't come to the next haiku meeting, or the next, or the next. But he didn't stop talking about *akigusa* at the college. We had to give up drinking tea in the faculty room. Sometimes we would try to creep in quietly when Mr. Okamoto wasn't there, but he always seemed to appear from somewhere before we could get away again. He wasn't interested, particularly, in convincing me, but it was often difficult to rescue Mr. Uematsu. When Mr. Okamoto trapped him, I would edge toward the door, then run soundlessly down the hall to the office and get the secretary to run back with a message. "Telephone, Uematsu *sensei*," she would shout.

Once, shopping in a department store, I heard the word *akigusa* in a conversation on the other side of the parasol counter. I looked around for Mr. Okamoto's back, but I could only see a clump of people I didn't recognize. Was his argument so pervasive that it was spreading all over Hiroshima? Or did everybody just talk about *akigusa* naturally, or was I hearing the word when it wasn't really there?

Meanwhile, at the haiku sessions, Uematsu–*sensei* was riding high. He had Mr. Hirokawa, the greatest haiku authority in Hiroshima, maybe in Japan, on his side. Mr. Kata had been subdued somewhat, and he had the foreigners firmly in their place, well aware of their limitations.

There was a poem about a person being urged forward by someone's backward glance amid barren, winter trees. I was waiting for Mr. Kata to describe the romantic elements with his usual pleasure. He didn't say anything at all. Nobody else seemed inclined to argue any more, either. And there was never any reason for Yoshi's diversionary exuberances. Maybe it was the haiku we were translating. There were no controversies in them. We always agreed. And besides, Mr. Hirokawa did most of the work. He usually came up with a good, sensitive final translation, and we accepted it. There was no excitement.

One afternoon I crept into the faculty room at the college and found Mr. Okamoto alone drinking his green tea. It had been three months since the autumn grass argument. The winter holidays were over, and we were settling in for a cold February and March, and for the suffering that always went with the entrance exams.

"The haiku sessions just aren't the same without you, Okamoto–*sensei*," I said, slipping down into a hulky, overstuffed western chair covered on the back by an antimacassar. He was surprised because nobody had dared mention the word "haiku" in his presence for quite some time. He looked up at me over the steam of his green tea and gave me his Cheshire cat smile, which, as I look back on it now, I realize was the only charming thing about him.

"No more fights, huh?" he said. He bit into a Japanese tea cake, and then carefully examined the red bean paste inside.

"No more fights," I echoed. There was a silence, so I looked into the tea pot, hoping for more tea, but it was all gone.

"Why don't you come again?" I asked. "Really, we miss you."

His smile faded.

"Oh, I don't mean for the fights," I said. "It's just that we feel lacking, not having you. We all want you to come, really," I lied. "We were just talking about you at the last meeting." We had done nothing of the kind. In fact, we had all been very careful to avoid discussing him.

What happened next might have happened whether Okamoto–*sensei* came again or not. Certainly he didn't contribute anything to the argument. He was just there.

The poem was about a spider web, and the morning sun shining in on a big circle:

> *Kumo no i ya*
> spider's web and

> *Asahi sashikite*
> morning sun comes shining (piercing?) through

> *dairin ni*
> big circle in

The *dairin ni* was ambiguous, because it could mean either "in the big circle" or it could be a shortened form of *dairin ni naru,* which would mean 'making' or "becoming a big circle."

"Spider web, and the morning sun comes shining into the big circle"

or maybe:

"Spider web, and the morning sun comes piercing in, illuminating a big circle"

Mr. Uematsu talked about the threads of the web glistening under the sun. He said he envisioned the sun thrusting itself into some dark, maybe decaying place, and then finding unexpected beauty there, making a glistening, circular, patterned design out of an ordinary old cobweb.

Mr. Hirokawa had been sitting serenely and quietly by the fire, gazing into it. "What is the seasonal word?" he asked us abruptly. Of course we waited for the answer he was so obviously going to provide. "Perhaps it is the spider web," he said, "but I think it is *dairin*."

The word *dairin*, he told us, of course meant a big circle literally. But everybody knew that it usually referred to the big circumference around the outside of a flower, any big round flower. Wasn't it rather that the sun was shining in, revealing the presence of a morning glory or some other kind of flower? It didn't *have* to be a morning glory, he said, but somehow to him, it fit with the spider web and the morning sun. Wasn't it more meaningful to contrast a fresh, new morning glory with an old, musty cobweb?

Mr. Uematsu's pipe nearly fell out of his mouth because it was so wide open. He said that bringing a morning glory into it was like sewing on a patch that was the wrong color. It was very forced. It was the most unsuitable thing he'd ever heard. It was worse than using flowers and delicate ladies instead of autumn grass and farmers. Of course *dairin* meant a flower in many circumstances, especially poetic ones. But he had always thought of *dairin* in connection with a chrysanthemum, not a morning glory. And the chrysanthemum was an autumn flower. The morning sun shining in on a musty spider web made you think immediately of spring, and of the lightness and warmth that came after the cold night of winter, not of autumn.

He was even willing to concede, he said that *dairin* could be translated as "flower" instead of "big circle", that the sun was shining in on the spider web, making it into a flower because of its glistening, exquisite pattern. Even that, he thought, was forced. But he would concede it. A morning glory? Never. He sat glaring at Mr. Hirokawa.

Mr. Kata said that, of course the poet, Teijo Nakamura, would be referring to a flower, not a big circle, and that personally he found the morning glory interpretation quite appealing. Mr. Okamoto sat nodding, not saying anything, but clearly agreeing with Mr. Kata.

Miss Taki said she didn't know. She wasn't sure. She couldn't decide. It was unusual for her. She had always been reluctant to walk in front of the professor's chairs, but not to oppose their opinions. Although, as I remember, she had never disagreed with Mr. Hirokawa.

Yoshi emitted some short, gutteral Japanese sounds, which were not familiar to me, and which Mr. Uematsu wouldn't translate, although Mr. Garnell and all the Japanese laughed. At least there was no doubt that he didn't think much of the Hirokawa interpretation.

It was all the support Mr. Uematsu seemed to be getting. The rest of us were silent.

Mr. Uematsu was looking toward Mr. Garnell, who shifted uneasily in his seat. "Well, there isn't much we can do about all this," Mr. Garnell said. "After all, if autumn grass really means autumn flowers, and if big circles also mean flowers, then who knows what else in Japanese, which isn't really a flower on the surface, is actually a flower underneath? How are we, as foreigners, ever supposed to know that? I mean, it seems to me, we could go on studying haiku and trying to translate it for twenty years, and we'd not be the better for it. We'd not be any more knowledgeable."

There was Mr. Uematsu's sweet revenge, lying there right in his lap. And from Mr. Garnell, too, not from the Eckelsbergs or me. But he didn't even want it any more. He wanted his plain, homely spider web, glistening in the sun, dew–strung.

There wasn't anything anybody could say. Somehow, the morning glory intrigued me, too. Not because the image was any more beautiful. Finding a flower where you least expected it. Maybe it was because of the surprise. Or maybe it was Mr. Hirokawa. His serene Tokugawa face and giant–like presence. He had always dazzled me.

"How about some tea?" I asked.

We drank some tea. But in a desultory, disinterested way. As if we had all come into a mountain tea house but from different paths and intended to follow different paths afterwards.

It was spring, and we were all caught up with one thing or another, finishing off the term before summer vacation. We had intended to have one more haiku session, but we all got too busy. By autumn, Mr. Garnell had gone home, and the Eckelsbergs were packing up and getting ready.

Mr. Uematsu suggested that we go on with the study group, reading English fiction. So we attacked that project anew, and as usual, he was alternately amazed and depressed by the twisted misbehaviour of the English language.

Maxine Zalkin
The Second Day of Autumn

She was lying on her back on the window seat, absent-mindedly looking up through the trees with their yellow leaves against the bright blue sky, almost October, and suddenly although it wasn't an experience of suddenness, there were three tiny shining white specks flowing by, way way up, one and then another and then the third, going exactly from north to south. She thought, "If I hadn't been looking up it would have happened without me." She tried to make more go by, first by waiting and then by willing them to appear, but nothing more followed. And then while she was looking, a seed held up by its fluff, floated by and she wondered if that is what the three had been, way way up there, but then another tiny bright white speck went by on that same stream south and then another and then a seed fluff drifted by and she didn't know what she was looking at. Was she looking at the flyway—the birds going south—way way up there or were her eyes distorting the distance because of the bright blue sky and was she only looking at seeds blowing by? But the movement of the one was quite different from the movement of the other and then a bright orange and black butterfly darted past. It would all have gone on without her if she hadn't been lying on her back on the window seat looking up through the trees on the second day of autumn.

Biographical Notes

These women writers have been meeting and working together for thirteen years.

SUE HEATH BROWN was born in Rumania of American Diplomatic Corps parents. Her childhood was spent in many countries. After graduation from Scripps College in Claremont, California, she worked for newspapers, won prizes at writers' conferences and raised a family. Her stories and poems have been published in *Across the Generations* and *Tunnel Road*. She has written four novels and is at work on a biography.

ALICE WIRTH GRAY is from Chicago and her first poetry teacher was Langston Hughes. She has received awards from the Arvon International Poetry Competition, the Poetry Society of America and the Illinois Arts Council. Her poetry has appeared in *The American Scholar*, *The Atlantic*, *Chelsea*, *Poetry* and *Breakfast without Meat*; fiction in *Helicon Nine* and *Primavera*. She lives with her husband in Berkeley.

MARY L. HANNER is a native of Minnesota and now lives in San Jose, California with her husband and children. Her poetry has appeared in *Cedar Rock*, *Impact*, *Northwoods Journal*, *In a Nutshell* and *California State Poetry Quarterly*. Her novel, *Premature*, was published by The New American Library (Signet) in 1981.

MARY TOLMAN KENT is a native of Berkeley where she lives with her husband. She has had stories published in *Impact*, *Collage*, *Expanding Horizons*, *Across the Generations* and is currently at work on her second novel.

MARY H. McLAUGHLIN is a native of Ireland. She has spent most of her life in New York City in the business world. She is now retired to Berkeley where she is writing stories and poems about her early life in Ireland. She has been published in *The Berkeley Monthly* and *Across the Generations*.

MOLLIE POUPENEY spent her childhood on the Oregon Coast, and was educated at Oregon State University and the University of California. Also a potter, she has written three articles about the primitive process for *Ceramics Monthly* magazine. She now lives in Moraga, California.

JANE STRONG was born in Chicago, lived in Hawaii. One of her plays was produced at San Francisco State University's Arena Theatre, and a one-act was circulated by Office of Advanced Drama Research. She has had fiction accepted by *Texas Quarterly* and *Primavera*, poetry in *Behold Hawaii, Tunnel Road, Blue Unicorn*, and the anthology of the Arvon International Poetry Competition. She is married and lives in Berkeley.

DOROTHY STROUP grew up in Colorado and was educated at Colorado College. She has master's degrees in Journalism and Asian Studies from U.C. Berkeley, and has taught in several colleges and countries, including Japan. Her novel, *In the Autumn Wind* was published by Scribner's in February 1987. She lives in Berkeley, California.

MAXINE ZALKIN spent her first twenty one years in Minnesota. She taught elementary school in Chicago and English to the foreign born in New York City. She spent one year in the desert in New Mexico before coming to the Bay Area. She is married and has two children. She has participated in a poetry reading in Berkeley and won honorable mention for a poem at the Northern California Poets' Dinner.

Order more copies of

My Neckline and the Collapse of Western Civilization

from

Smartweed Press
81 Edgecroft Road
Kensington, California 94707